H

The
IRONSTONE QUARRIES
of the
MIDLANDS

History, Operation and Railways

Part II
The Oxfordshire Field
by
Eric Tonks
M.Sc., F.R.I.C., Dip.Maths.

Runpast Publishing
Cheltenham

© Eric Tonks

April 1988

Tonks, Eric S. (Eric Sidney), *1914-*
 The Ironstone Quarries of the Midlands:
 History, operation and railways.
 Pt. 2: Oxfordshire
 1. England. Midlands. Iron quarries, to 1980.
 I. Title
 622'.341'09424

 ISBN 1-870754-02-6

Produced for the Publishers by
Mopok Graphics
128 Pikes Lane
Glossop, Derbyshire
Printed in Great Britain

Smoke drifts lazily from the chimney of Hudswell Clarke locomotive MARY as she pushes up 'dumpcars' to be loaded by the 100RB electric shovel in the Balscott Quarry of Oxfordshire Ironstone Co Ltd. The ironstone here is only a few feet below the surface, and the worked-out area to the left has already been restored to cultivation. In the background can be seen a 43RB diesel dragline stripping the topsoil to expose the stone beneath. About 1953.

(British Steel Corporation)

CONTENTS

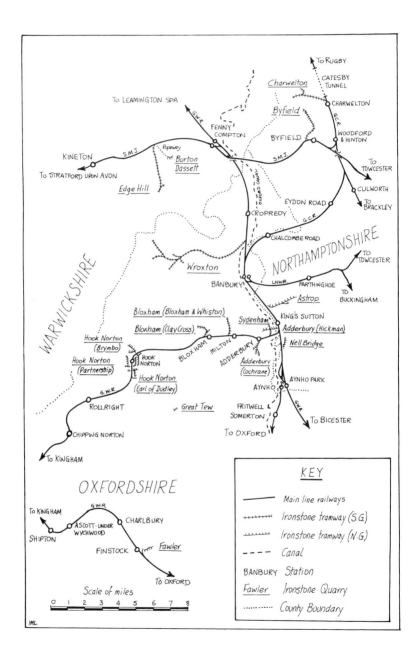

KEY

——————	Main line railways
+++++++	Ironstone tramway (S.G.)
⊢⊢⊢⊢⊢	Ironstone tramway (N.G.)
- - - -	Canal
BANBURY	Station
Fawler	Ironstone Quarry
....	County Boundary

INTRODUCTION

The Oxfordshire Field

The ironstone in the vicinity of Banbury and southwards is generally referred to as the Oxfordshire Field, though in fact it spills over into Warwickshire and Northamptonshire; but the close relationships between the various workings makes it logical to study them as a group, the history of which extends over nearly the same period as that in Northamptonshire, starting a few years later and ceasing a few years earlier. The area thus defined was isolated geographically from the other Midlands ironstone fields and developed independently of them, with its own markets, the chief being the ironworks of Staffordshire and South Wales.

The influence of the main line railways in quarry development is shown very clearly. Except for the curiously isolated working at Fawler on the Oxford, Worcester and Wolverhampton Railway, the early workings were close to the Great Western Railway main line from Paddington to the Midlands, in the vicinity of Kings Sutton, including three in Northamptonshire; and the Oxford Canal also played a part in taking ore to the West Midlands. The Banbury & Cheltenham Direct Railway passed through country rich in ironstone, but it was a long time a-building, in the course of which plans to open up quarries at Bloxham were shelved; but when at last in 1887 the through line was opened there was intense activity at Adderbury and Hook Norton, both with complex transport arrangements, in the case of Adderbury involving canal as well as rail. Bloxham was eventually opened up in World War I, when the increased demand led also to developments to the east in Northamptonshire at Byfield and Charwelton, the former served by the Stratford upon Avon & Midland Junction Railway and the latter the sole ironstone quarry on the Great Central Railway; and the major orefield west of Banbury exploited, with vastly differing success, by Oxfordshire Ironstone and by the Edge Hill Light Railway. Warwickshire's contribution to ironstone production was very small, but any shortcomings in this direction were transcended by the great interest of the transport arrangements in getting the ore to the SMJ; Burton Dassett with its ropeway and numerous successive owners, and the EHLR with its rope-worked incline, its status as a Light Railway, and its long period of dereliction.

The isolation of the Oxfordshire Field is reflected in many ways. Narrow gauge tramways, for example, were based on two foot rather than the three foot or metre gauges common elsewhere, and locomotive liveries included maroon and grey among the usual greens. Another prominent feature, practically confined to this area, was the use of calcining kilns to dry the ore. Again, because of the distance from other ironstone fields, there was little interchange of personnel, to whom Corby was as remote as Middlesbrough. It is an area that can be studied in its own right, and in this sort of countryside there is little inducement to go elsewhere. The stone belongs to the Marlstone Rock formation and, as in Leicestershire, was usually under shallow overburden that even in the latest quarries only required modest mechanical equipment for removal; there were none of the 'hill and dale' wastelands that earned such a bad name for parts of Northamptonshire between the wars. There were no ironworks, though Banbury was considered as an alternative to Corby by Stewarts & Lloyds Ltd when choosing a site for their new steelworks in the 1930s; in Oxfordshire, ironstone was always purely an industry of the countryside, one of its greatest attractions to students and enthusiasts, who regret its passing as much as the quarrymen.

Generally speaking, the area is well served for information, particularly for the quarries dating from World War I. Oxfordshire Ironstone Co Ltd was the largest producer of iron ore outside Corby and when it came to its untimely end the manager donated all the office files to the Oxfordshire County Archivist, who redistributed them as appropriate; they form the most complete record we have of a working ironstone system. Its rail system of near mainline standard had been a magnet for industrial locomotive and railway enthusiasts since the 1930s, so we have plenty of day-to-day observations of its operations. Its unfortunate neighbour at Edge Hill hardly produced any iron ore at all, but the status of its rail system as a Statutory Light Railway and the presence of two ex-LBSCR 'Terrier' locomotives was enough to ensure plenty of attention from enthusiasts for study and photography. Byfield, Charwelton and Bloxham (Milton) quarries are all covered in BSC archives and the other Bloxham in Clay Cross Co's private archives, with of course people on the spot. For the rest we have to rely more on local sources and in this we are fortunate in having for the Adderbury area the energetic local historian J. J. Fox; and for Hook Norton the Local History Group, who have been very active in assembling information, photographs and relics. Fawler, well away from any other ironstone quarry, seems to have captured the imagination of anyone who has visited the site; 'Liassic Ironstones' gives a detailed account of its history and it has been the subject of student 'projects'. The quarries in the Kings Sutton district of Northamptonshire are less favoured, and the search for information had to be conducted on site to a large extent; so too for Burton Dassett in Warwickshire.

My interest in the area is deep and of longstanding; Burton Dassett was the first ironstone quarry I saw, Edge Hill the second and Wroxton the third, going back fifty years or more, and giving me an abiding love for this countryside. Always a pleasure to visit; and an equal pleasure to meet the people who have contributed so much of the information, as acknowledged in the text. My thanks also to the staff of Oxfordshire County Record Office, Banbury Reference Library, and the proprietors of *'The Banbury Guardian'*.

Birmingham, 1988   Eric Tonks

Readers' attention is drawn to the explanation of abbreviations in the text and terms used in tables of locomotives and equipment, listed on pages 242-245.

The maps have all been prepared by Ian Lloyd

KEY TO INDIVIDUAL QUARRY MAPS

————————— Main line railway.

BY FIELD Station.

+++++++++ Ironstone tramway (standard gauge).

⊥⊥⊥⊥⊥⊥ Ironstone tramway (narrow gauge).

⊥⊥⊥⊥⊥⊥ Ironstone tramway (rope worked incline).

– – – Canal.

⊥ ⊥ Roads.

Byfield Village.

Byfield Quarries Ironstone Quarry.

Area of Quarry working.

Redlands Quarry face.

┌ 1919
│
▼ 1928 Direction of quarrying and dates of operation.

SOUTHERN GROUP
The Blenheim Iron Ore

FAWLER QUARRIES AND MINES

**Owners: Unknown; Fawler Iron Ore Co Ltd
(Bolton & Partners Ltd) from 1880.**

The Fawler ironstone workings were the first in Oxfordshire, only six years after the start in Northamptonshire, and, like the other early workings in the county, were close to a railway—in this case the Oxford, Worcester and Wolverhampton Railway, whose Wolvercot Junction to Evesham section was opened for traffic 4th June 1853. It was hoped that the quarries would alleviate the financial difficulties of the OWWR[1] and that the opening of the Worcester and Hereford route would encourage a heavy ore traffic to South Wales[2]. Neither of these expectations was fully realised, as the output was small, but operations at Fawler attracted a lot of attention from geologists both at the time and later; the account in LI is the most detailed in the book, which in general concentrates on the currect position, with a summary of past events. There could be a number of reasons for this unusual interest in Fawler; the isolation of the site from any other workings (it was even called 'the Blenheim Ore'), its very attractive location in the beautiful Evenlode valley, and the mystery surrounding its development. In addition to ironstone, this small site has yielded clay for brickmaking and limestone for burning, all leaving characteristic traces.

There were two distinct phases of operation, but of the first little is known other than the dates 1858 to April 1866 quoted in MS. This source does not give any owner's name, merely quoting the site as 'Fawler & Charlbury', but there is no record of any quarries other than those at Fawler; possibly the entry in MS is a slip for Fawler (Charlbury) as appears against the later period, Fawler being but a tiny hamlet. The quarries lay between the hamlet and the river and were served by a siding running northwest from a point about 400 yards on the Oxford side of Finstock Halt, though the latter did not then exist, being a comparatively recent GWR introduction. The 1884 6in. OS shows this siding and on its east side 'Ironstone Mines (disused)'; the hatching on the map suggests that a tramway was used, but if so it could only have

11

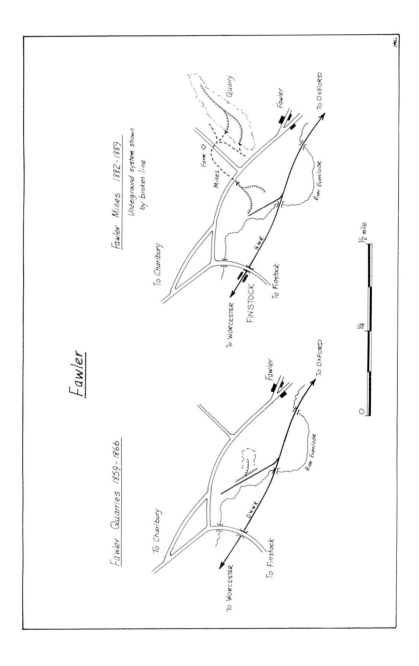

been a very small one, possibly with small wooden tubs propelled by hand to the railway siding. LI states that it is the spoil from these outcrop workings that now forms a tree-topped ridge along the river bank; this must have been carried over the railway siding. Commercial production commenced in 1859. The output went to South Staffordshire[3] but in total only amounted to just over 30,000 tons. It is possible that increasing overburden caused cessation of working, and the site lay dormant until 1880, when a lease to work ironstone was granted by the Duke of Marlborough to Lt. Col. F. J. Bolton. The nine-acre field known as Ashey Close, worked in the 1858-66 period, is shown on the 1847 Tithe map as occupied by William Bolton[4], a presumed ancestor. The new lease of March 1880 covered a larger area, but was replaced in September 1882 by an extended lease covering between 500 and 600 acres north, northwest and northeast of Fawler, and a small area between river and railway south-south-west of the hamlet; this area was considerably reduced under a third lease of 1884, granted to Sir F. J. Bolton. This information was supplied by the Land Agent of Blenheim Estates and quoted in LI.

The quarries are listed in MS under the style of Bolton & Partners Ltd and in production for the years 1882-86; the site is also listed as a mine under the Metalliferous Mines Regulations Act, from 1886-88, but with zero production. The ledgers of the Birmingham Railway Carriage & Wagon Co Ltd, in Staffordshire Record Office, record the leasing of 100 18-ton railway wagons to Fawler Iron Ore Co Ltd in 1881, with purchase completed in 1886. Of the operating history of this period we have the recollections of old employees very fortunately recorded by geologists. In 1942 Mr T. H. Whitehead (contributing the account on pp 197–8 in LI) obtained information from Mr William Paintin, who as a boy of sixteen worked in the 'mine' as a pony driver, while in 1945 Dr W. J. Arkell interviewed Mr Fred Oliver, born in 1874 at Finstock and whose father was employed on the ironstone[5]. As usual, these accounts and that of another and much earlier geologist, J. D. Kendall[6], do not tally completely, but Mr Whitehead has deduced the probable sequence of events, aided by annotations to the 1884 lease at Blenheim Palace. We obtained further information from Mr Oliver (who died in November 1955) and from his niece, Mrs Eden.

The first working of the 1880 period was a large quarry northwest of the hamlet, east of the road, from which the output was conveyed overland—by carts presumably—to the GWR siding; there may also have been a resumption of working at the old site between road and railway. Then a tunnel was driven from the northwest side of the main quarry, under the road, and the tramway laid through this to the railway siding; attempts were made to mine the ore in galleries branching from the tunnel, and a plan attached to the 1884 lease shows in pencil lines that represent the tunnel and branch galleries. How much ore came from underground is uncertain, for while none is listed in the mining returns, Mr. Oliver was of the opinion that a good deal of ore was so obtained; it is possible that the outputs of both quarry and mine were combined in the quarry returns. The gauge of the tramway was between 2ft. and 2ft. 6in., and the side-tipping 'dubbing' wagons, some of wood and some of iron, were hauled by ponies to an elevated tipping dock alongside the GWR siding.

The quarries were closed in 1885, probably as a result of the collapse of the tunnel, which took place at night, burying tools and wagons inside. The company also made bricks and pottery etc, obtaining their material from a claypit between railway and road, and it is possible that this side of the business was continued after the cessation of ironstone traffic. According to Mr. Oliver, the final breakup was attributable to a disagreement between the partners, and the lease was surrendered in 1892. The GWR siding was removed shortly afterwards, but the ironstone tramway survived until World War II, when it was taken up for scrap.

Considering that a century has gone by since quarrying ceased, it is perhaps surprising that any traces remain, but they do; not as many as 30 years ago, but still enough to make a visit worthwhile. The GWR siding route is clearly defined, though heavily overgrown with trees, and the course of the tramway is indicated by a slightly built-up formation. The claypit on this side is now a pond, and the surrounding ground is hummocky from the old workings. The more deeply quarried a____ ___with gullets still visible, is also covered with trees; the tunnel m__ ___nger be seen, but the high ground between trees an____ apparent 'sink holes' along the line of tunnel and____ large quarry east of the road is still identifiable, though it____ adually being filled in with waste from the new dairy farm on the site; this and other changes in land usage have obliterated the pits in the surface, between the quarry and the orchard to the southwest, where the tunnels have caved in. However, in 1982, the course of the tramway along the quarry floor towards the tunnel was still very well defined. The site between railway and road has been used for ironstone quarrying, limeburning and brickmaking at various times, and traces of all these can be made out, as described in Mike Aston's paper of 1971 on *The Fawler Industrial Site, Oxfordshire*. In 1982 we picked up here a brick incised 'Bolton & Partners Ltd, Charlbury', while Mrs Eden still has a hand-decorated plant pot made by the company; and among the trees in 1986 was a piece of tram rail, 1in. across the foot, 2in. high and ½in. across the head.

Footnotes

1. Banbury Guardian, 6th January 1859.
2. Mining Journal, 28th July 1860, p 511.
3. E. Hull, *On the Blenheim Iron Ore*. The Geologist, 1860, p 304.
4. *The Fawler Industrial Site, Oxfordshire*. Mike Aston, 1971.
5. W. J. Arkell, *The Geology of Oxford*. Clarendon Press, Oxford, 1947, p 19.
6. J. D. Kendall, *The Iron Ores of Great Britain and Ireland*. 1893, p 226.

Grid References

360170	Junction with main line railway
360171	Tunnel mouth west of road
361172	Tunnel mouth east of road
362712	Later Quarry (1882-5)—north end

The Kings Sutton Area

Adderbury was the second area of Oxfordshire to be opened up; the GWR main line was close at hand to provide transport, and so was the Oxford canal, and in the early days both were used; later, development was helped by the Banbury & Cheltenham Direct line, opened in 1887. The ironstone outcrop lies on the high ground on each side of the Cherwell, here forming the boundary between Oxfordshire and Northamptonshire; we have however dealt with all the quarries in this volume because of the close links in their histories. Apart from Aynho, which is something of a mystery, all the sites were interesting from the transport angle, with narrow gauge tramway systems possessing unusual features—and, in the case of Adderbury quarries, with complex histories.

NELL BRIDGE QUARRIES

Owners: Kings Sutton Ironstone Co; Nell Bridge Iron Ore Co from 1873.

These quarries to the east of the GWR main line lay in Northamptonshire, as does Kings Sutton village, and we use the title by which they were generally known locally; in MS they are quoted as Kings Sutton quarries for 1870-72. A further point is that MS has two entries for 1872, one under Northamptonshire as Kings Sutton Ironstone Co, with David Vincent Steuart as Manager, and one under Oxfordshire as Kings Sutton Iron Ore Co, with D. V. Steuart. The double entry for what is apparently the same place is possibly attributable to ownership. Adderbury Ironstone Co applied to Brackley Highway Board for permission to cross the road at Kings Sutton (*Northampton Mercury*, 16th September 1870); a month later (*ibid*, 8th October 1870) permission was granted to Kings Sutton Ironstone Co "to lay down a tramway at Watergate, provided it is done under the supervision of the Surveyor, and put under the road". From this it would appear that Adderbury Ironstone Co, based in Oxfordshire, owned Kings Sutton

Ironstone Co in Northamptonshire. The ground is believed to have belonged to Lord North of Wroxton Abbey.

The Nell Bridge quarries lay three quarters of a mile south of Kings Sutton church, and consisted of a narrow excavation along the eastern side of the lane from Kings Sutton Cemetery to the Banbury-Buckingham road, and from them a tramway was laid, passing under the lane on Watergate Hill by a skew brick arch and running down a slight slope to a bridge over the Cherwell to an elevated tipping dock alongside a GWR siding; a total length of about a third of a mile. Of the tramway equipment the only recorded details are from the Nell Bridge Iron Ore Co's prospectus, which states that £700 had been spent on the tramway (including the tunnel and the viaduct); that 38 trucks of one-ton capacity had been taken over from their predecessors; and that there were '940 laid sleepers and 196ft. of laid rail' (*Mining Journal*, 9th May 1874, p 500). No motive power is mentioned but the almost uniform gradient between the pits and loading stage suggests gravity working, probably with horses to haul up empties and to deal with wagons at the stage; the line would hardly be long enough to require a locomotive and there is no smoke-blackening on the tunnel roof.

The quarries are first mentioned in MS for 1870, and last in 1874. In this year the Nell Bridge Iron Ore Co issued a circular describing the 'extensive properties' and the value of their ore both as a self-fluxing furnace charge and in admixture with more refractory (less limey) ores; but little was done and the pits were presumably closed down in 1874, though some wagons and rails remained for many years; they are mentioned in the 1880s[1] and recalled by Miss May Hermon from the early 1900s.

The most easily identifiable remnant of this small system is the tunnel under the road; this has been filled in beneath but the west side parapet is pretty complete (1982) and even visible from passing trains, and consists of red brick with capping of concrete sloped along the sides and at the ends. The east side parapet has been demolished and the only traces are concrete blocks still lying among the trees that line the road northwards for about 300 yards; these trees are on a low embankment seemingly thrown up in the course of quarrying, and on the field side of them is a shallow gullet (with its usual complement of rubbish) that at the lower end drops down to tunnel level. There is a gap in the line of trees at one point for field access and the hedge that comes up to this point has been replaced by a wooden fence for some

30 yards, possibly indicating the extent of quarrying. On the other side of the road a shallow groove runs over the field down towards the river but there is no trace of the bridge; but alongside the BR line can be seen the quite substantial embankment for the tipping stage, though this formation was damaged in 1958–9 in connection with road bridge widening. The embankment seems to be higher than necessary and may have derived from the nearby railway cutting when the GWR line was built.

Footnote

1. Beeby Thompson; *The Middle Lias of Northamptonshire*—Victoria County History, II, p 307.

Grid References

497343	Tipping Dock by GWR—south end
499346	Bridge under road
500349	Gullet—north end

Nell Bridge Quarries.
The bridge on Watergate Hill. Kings Sutton, from the west. The quarries lay beyond the trees on the far side of the road, and from this side the line ran down to the GWR. 6th September 1975.

(Eric Tonks)

ASTROP QUARRIES

Owners: Alfred Hickman Ltd.

Like Nell Bridge to the south of Kings Sutton, Astrop quarries were in Northamptonshire, and an area of 319 acres in Kings Sutton parish was leased by Sir William Richard Brown, Bart, of Astrop Hall, to Alfred Hickman Ltd for a period of 21 years from 25th March 1896. The leased land lay 1 to 1½ miles north of Kings Sutton, mostly around the 400ft. contour and about 100ft. above the the level of the GWR main line, to which the output was consigned. As described in the *Banbury Guardian* of 24th February 1898, the transfer arrangements, unique among ironstone quarries, were made at a point 1⅓ miles north of Kings Sutton station, where the ground slopes down sharply to the main line. Most of the ore was to be calcined, and three 65ft. high Gyers kilns were erected alongside the railway, where the GWR put in a simple layout of two sidings for full wagons, one for empties and with a loop line round the kilns between the two; the whole controlled from Astrop Siding Box. Within the sidings, gravity working was used. From the ironstone pits a 2ft. 1in-gauge tramway[1] was laid; where the ground fell away, the central line of tramway was carried on a 240-yard long viaduct to the top of the kilns, over each of which a tippler was installed so that wagons could be emptied directly into the kilns. A mixture of coal slack and ore was introduced thus, and after the calcining process, taking two to three months, the ore was loaded into standard gauge wagons via chutes at the feet of the kilns and controlled by levers. Slack was stored in bunkers by the GWR siding and transferred thence to narrow gauge wagons for transport up the hill. The narrow gauge line also had two branches to the foot of the first kiln. Each kiln held 600 tons and was of steel plates lined with firebrick. A certain amount of ore was sent away in the raw state, wagons of this being lowered to railway level via a cable-worked incline with a tipping dock at the foot. In 1898/9 two more kilns were added[2]. In the early days the tops of the kilns were continually obscured by steam but later on they were covered to avoid this.

The tramway was of double track, and haulage was by endless steel cable driven by a steam engine at the kilns; at the farther end the cable passed round a wheel that was pushed forward in stages as quarrying took place further from the GWR. Wagons were brought from the

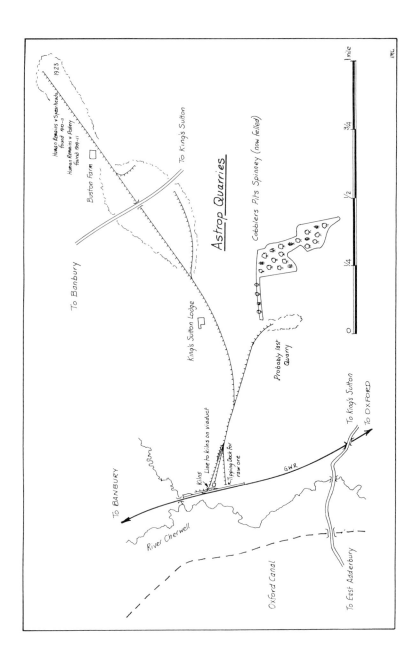

working faces to the cableway by single line branches, for which purpose about a dozen horses were kept. The Inventory dated 18th September 1903 lists stabling, not included in the 1899 New Inventory, so perhaps horses were not used for the first few years when the working faces were closer to the main cableway — or else horses were returned each night to local farmers. Wagons were of steel, approximately one yard square and holding 21 cwt, and were attached singly to the cable by means of a clip worked by a lever, and could be detached without stopping the cable; when required to be lowered down the incline at the railway terminus, they were attached to the incline cable in pairs and the loaded ones brought up empties in the usual way. The OS does not show lineside hedges throughout, but some means of keeping animals away from the tramway would be necessary, and there would probably be some form of telegraph system for contacting the engineman out of sight of the quarries, as was done at Orton and Cranford Clay Cross quarries. The tubs were oiled automatically; small tanks of oil were laid at intervals between the rails and in each tank two wheels were arranged so that they revolved, transferring oil to the axles passing over them.

Construction work began in August 1896 and production commenced 4th July 1897. An output of just under 80,000 tons in 1898 swelled to over 100,000 tons in 1899, of which about two thirds was calcined. All of it is believed to have gone to Hickman's Springvale Furnaces at Bilston. In the absence of the annual surveyor's maps, information on the succession of working areas is fragmentary. From the viaduct the tramway took a southward course and then swung round in a long gentle curve to pass on the south side of Kings Sutton Lodge, then east-north-east on a practically straight course; with cable haulage it is desirable to avoid sharp curves as much as possible, to reduce wear on guide rollers. The tramway passed beneath the Astrop-Warkworth lane close to the drive to Buston Farm, crossing the drive en route.

The OS map incorporating revisions of 1920 shows on the southwest side of this crossing 'Old ironstone quarry', which is probably one of the early workings, and the present day configuration of the ground suggests others on the northwest side. Sunken fields are also to be seen on both sides of Buston Farm on the other side of the road, and here the 1923 6in. OS gives us a clue with notes of finds of 'human remains, pottery and spearheads' over the period 1909-11 at three points close to the tramway route. This map shows the main tramway terminating at a point a third of a mile east-north-east of Buston Farm, with the footpath from Middleton Cheney to Astrop crossing the workings by a footbridge. GSM and LI refer to these operations, quoting the year 1913, but as the OS was carried out in 1920 it seems that work was still in progress then, as the quarries are not shown as 'disused'. The total length of the main tramway was then 1¾ miles, but locomotive power was never introduced in spite of its being used at the nearby Sydenham Quarries owned by the same company. According to LI, the last quarry is believed to have been between King's Sutton Lodge and Cobbler's Pit Spinney, and this is probably borne out by a 6in. map preserved at Bilston, showing a pit running south from the northern end of a grove of trees extending from Cobbler's Pit Spinney; the tramway is shown curving away from this pit, then making an almost straight run to the viaduct, and the line to Buston Farm is not shown at all, having presumably been lifted. As this map is undated, however, it could possibly apply to very early days **before** the Buston Farm line was laid.

The pits were always shallow and in general the working depth was less than the 20ft. maximum permissible to obviate compliance with the Quarries Acts; nevertheless the work was hard and the pay small—4d per ton of wet ore, 3½d for dry, 20 tons per day being the average output per man; 3d per yard for 'baring' (removing overburden) and ¼d each for tipping wagons. At first the topsoil was removed by a Priestman's steam digger fitted with a 'claw' (presumably an early form of clamshell attachment) but about 1900 a Wilson long-jib steam excavator, of the type introduced by Lloyds Ironstone Co Ltd, was obtained—rather surprisingly for so modest and little-known a system to be in the forefront of mechanical excavation. Barnes[3] states that it was supplied to Alfred Hickman & Co Ltd for use in their 'ironstone mines near Banbury', which would apply to Astrop at this time. However, the experiment seems to have been less successful than at Corby, for GSM (1917) records handworking only. The same source mentions hand working also at Sydenham quarries, so it would seem that the machine was not moved thence.

Labour difficulties caused suspension of activities from February to September 1921 but demand was falling by then anyway. The original lease expired in 1917 but evidently an extension of time had been granted, as the records at Bilston include negotiations with Mr. F. B. Brown (Sir William having died in 1921) as 'the present lease expires in March 1923'. A further three years was requested to complete the removal of available stone but only one year was granted. Closure in

Astrop Quarries. The only visible reminder of this system is the tipping dock alongside the GWR line south of Banbury. It was used for the transhipment of raw ore, most of the output being calcined in kilns. 17th March 1981. (Eric Tonks)

March 1924 can be inferred from this, supported by the evidence of a GWR Sidings Diagram dated 12th November 1924, showing the main line connection removed and the signal box renamed Astrop Signal Box[4]. The known workable remains were down to less than a quarter of a million tons by 1920, but another factor in the closure was the acquisition by Alfred Hickman Ltd of a 50 per cent interest in Oxfordshire Ironstone Co Ltd, who from 1925 supplied all their ironstone requirements from the Banbury area[5].

The tramway was dismantled and there are few traces to be seen today, as earthworks of any consequence were not called for. At the BR end the only recognisable remnant is the tipping dock of ironstone blocks, where raw ore was tipped into railway wagons; of the more important transfer from kilns there is nothing to be seen other than the site of the sidings, and even this looks pitifully small to have accommodated five kilns; one wonders how they got them in the space ... Around Buston Farm sunken fields on both sides of the lane show where ironstone was quarried, those to the south of the farm crossed by wire fences in lieu of hedges. The point where the tramway passed beneath the lane can be identified, with nearby, on the southwest side, the former stables. Three hundred yards along the lane on the same side, towards Astrop, the limit of working can be seen, and along it a double line of hedge—just possibly where the branch tramway ran. The terminal face can be seen to curve away from the little spinney to the south, and close to this a replacement hedge of hawthorn and elder shows a dip. Fields further south and west are below their former level, but of the believed final gullet there is no trace at all, while most of the northern part of Cobbler's Pit Spinney has been felled, not for ironstone extraction but for agricultural expansion. Not a lot to see, therefore, but a very pleasant walk.

Footnotes

1. Richard Thomas & Baldwins Ltd, Irthlingborough files in BSC archives. 'Inspection of Calcining Kilns' Report 10th September 1915.
2.*Banbury Guardian* 23rd June 1898 and 4th June 1899. Also, Inventory of 1897 and New Inventory of 1899 in the Drawing Office records at Bilston Steelworks. (Courtesy of Alan Wilkes and Douglas Martin).
3. W. Barnes, 'Excavating Machinery in the Ironstone Fields'; reprinted from *The Engineer*, August 1942.
4. Mr A. Batts; letter 12th March 1961.
5. Sir Frederick Scopes; letter 16th March 1966.

Grid References

486379	Tipping dock to GWR
486380	Kilns—north end
489379	Viaduct—east end
502385	Bridge under road by Buston Farm; also stables
511391	Terminus of tramway
502383	Dip in replacement hedge on site of former quarry

Quarry machines

S. Stripping Shovel. Long Jib. Wilson   c.1890 1½ Cu.Yds. 70ft. New c.1890 s/s

S. Navvy. Clamshell.   Priestman c.1897 1 Cu. Yd.   New c.1897 s/s

AYNHO QUARRY

Owners: Lovel & Roseby

Ironstone quarrying at Aynho is recorded in MS for the years 1870-74 under the ownership of Lovel & Roseby, with as Manager W. J. Roseby, a name associated with a number of ironstone operations, e.g. Nevill Holt and Nettleton; mainly in isolated and rather out-of-the-way locations. In the case of Aynho this is the sum total of our knowledge, not even the site being known. The pleasant village of Aynho lies about a mile from the Great Western Railway station of that name, standing on high ground that includes an outcrop of the Marlstone Rock, and it seems likely that the quarry was here; but there are no present indications in the well-tilled fields and pastures, nor of any tramway towards the GWR, which at this time would have been to the older route to Oxford, not the cut off via Princes Risborough.

ADDERBURY QUARRIES

Owners: The Adderbury Ironstone Co; Alfred Hickman Ltd from 1889

Up to 1900 the various workings at Adderbury were listed in MS and LQ as 'Adderbury Quarries', a title used also in other references without discrimination even when more than one were operating at the same time; this accords with ironstone quarry nomenclature (as for the various 'Eaton Quarries' and 'Blisworth Quarries' for example) but the revived workings of World War II were, by a reversal of custom, always known as Sydenham Quarries.

Adderbury Quarries are listed in MS along with Fawler and Steeple Aston as being in production in 1859, the first year that Oxfordshire appears in the record; in 1859 3,410 tons of ore were despatched from Adderbury and in the following year 1,250 tons (including the output of Steeple Aston) and nil for 1861. The quarry lay immediately adjacent to the Buckingham road, on the north east side, and the output carried over a short narrow gauge tramway to a wharf on the Oxford Canal knows as 'Adderbury Stone Quarry'[1]. MS does not give the owner's name but in 1872 the landowner was Edward Railton; and Mr. J. J. Fox, of Adderbury, confirms that Railton farmed this land.

Production is recorded again in MS for 1869 under the style of The Adderbury Ironstone Co, and in a much bigger way, starting at 10,000 tons for that year; working of the old quarry continued under the new ownership, but the increase in output derived from the opening up of a much larger area to the north between East Adderbury and the canal. These quarries came to the notice of Samuel Lloyd, described in his *Reminiscences*[2] and quoted by Sir Frederick Scopes[3].

The quarries were then sending ore to Parkfield Ironworks near Wolverhampton. Mr Lloyd learnt that there were two properties, one being worked by a Cornish mining agent and the other by a Birmingham man; he acquired both properties and retained the services of both men to work them. The date of this transaction is not noted, but Birmingham Railway Carriage & Wagon Co Ltd leased railway wagons to 'Samuel Lloyd, trading as The Adderbury Ironstone Co' for 1869-77, so it appears that Mr Lloyd took over almost as soon as the quarries had reopened. The ore went away by canal and by rail, and operations went on until the stone was approaching exhaustion;

there is a sudden drop in production between 1877 and 1878 but the quarries were not closed until 1881. Beeby Thompson (*Journal of Northamptonshire Natural History Society, 1880-81*, p.277) states of the quarries "I believe they are worked at the present time by Mr Lloyd of Towcester", but his observations were probably made some time before appearing in print; Samuel Lloyd was operating at Towcester by 1877.

The first available OS map, for 1881, shows a tramway of some maturity, two thirds of a mile in length, running eastwards from an extensive quarry area on the west side of the Buckingham road to the GWR main line just south of Kings Sutton station; at this time this was the only railway in the vicinity, but there were two obstacles between quarry and railway — the Oxford canal and the River Cherwell. There was a spur to a wharf on the west bank of the canal and, 200 yards west of this, another spur led to a locomotive shed; the map also shows a northerly branch to a disused quarry (presumably older than that beyond the Buckingham road) and a weighbridge. The canal was crossed by 'Swing Bridge No. 182'. The older tramway (on Railton's land) does not appear on the 1881 map — only the disused quarry. For information between 1869 and 1881 we have by a lucky chance the Deposited Plans of the Banbury & Cheltenham Direct Railway, dated 28th November 1872. These show the earlier tramway to the canal, and, of the later one, the transfer arrangements at Kings Sutton. The latter comprised 'Tramway, ironstone shoot, turntable and siding over railway' — giving a fairly clear picture; as a wagon arrived from the pits it was put on the turntable and hauled up to a point above the railway siding where the contents could be dropped into a wagon via the 'shoot'. Rather a clumsy and laborious method, but labour was cheap in those days. The 'occupiers' of both system are quoted as 'The Adderbury Ironstone Co and Samuel Lloyd'.

Mr. J. J. Fox records (*'Adderbury Contact'*, Vol. 5, No. 9, September 1983) that his grandfather worked in the quarries in the 1860-70 period and remembered the wagons being taken to the main line, and occasionally falling into the canal on the way — to the vocal annoyance of boatmen when their craft were fouled. The lowlying and marshy ground between canal and railway shows no sign of a tramway, which would have had to be raised above ground level; earthworks would surely leave some traces, but there are none, so possibly the tramway was on wooden trestles for this section. We must here interpolate the recollections of Miss May Hermon, who as a girl was taken to King's Sutton station about 1910 by her father and shown where at one time 'buckets of ironstone came swinging through the air' behind the Down platform — clearly speaking of an aerial ropeway. Some substance to this account is provided by the obviously artificial mound of earth behind the platform; this has a perimeter path where one can imagine a man stationed to 'right' the buckets for the return journey to the quarries, after tipping their loads into wagons at the GWR siding. However, the evidence for the through tramway is so conclusive that it must be accepted and where Miss Hermon's information fits into the scheme is undetermined — and very probably, because of its being third hand, there has been some misinterpretation.

Details of tramway operation on the larger system are rather nebulous, so long a time having elapsed before enquiry was made. The gauge is said to have been quite small, 2ft. or less; it might have been 2ft. 1in., the odd gauge adopted by Hickman's in Astrop Quarries. Haulage is described by different informants as 'by horse and a small steam locomotive' or 'by gravity when full, by locomotive back to the quarries'. We can only assume that both these methods were employed; the topography rules out gravity working all the way from the pits, but there was a bank down to the canal, and the locomotive was kept at the summit of this bank. It seems very likely that horses were used to bring wagons from the pits to the vicinity of the locomotive shed, and then gravity allowed to take over and the locomotive used to haul back the empties. On the smaller and older line to the canal the tubs were probably pushed by hand the couple of hundred yards or so to the wharf.

In 1889 the quarries were taken over by Alfred Hickman Ltd, who introduced yet another method of transport; by this time the Kings Sutton-Chipping Norton line was open for traffic, providing a means of putting ore on rail without crossing the canal; the ore was loaded into barges at the wharf, taken a few hundred yards round the bend to the south and the stone then transferred to railway wagons at a wharf connected by a siding with the south side of the new railway, opposite Sydenham Farm. As described in the Sydenham Quarries section, there is reason to believe that Hickmans were using this method at the closure of Adderbury quarries. There are a number of uncertainties in this reconstruction of the transport methods at Adderbury, and we can give the data as we have them in the hope that someone else may be able to resolve them.

The 1881 OS shows the tramway crossing the Buckingham road on the level; on the west side of the road just at this point, there is now a small spinney on the worked-out ground at lower level. The 1881 map must represent pretty well the full extent of Adderbury Ironstone Co's activities, and Hickman evidently extended the line under the narrow lane to Bo Peep Farm to work ground to the north. How long they operated here is uncertain; MS lists them up to 1896, but there is no mention in LQ—but the workings were probably too shallow to require listing in any case. J. D. Kendall, in *Iron Ores of Great Britain & Ireland*, 1893, p.226, states that work had been suspended during a period of depression in the industry but they were reopened, as the *Banbury Guardian* of 3rd March 1898 reports the find of a large number of fossils in the quarries, which are also listed in *Kelly's Directory* for 1899; and Mr Flint, of Twyford, stated that they were being worked in 1900 when he left school to start work on a farm

Adderbury Quarries. Alfred Hickman took over the quarries in 1889, by which time the Banbury-Chipping Norton line was open and the ore was sent by canal to be loaded on to the line opposite Sydenham Farm. Picture shows traces of the former wharf, 27th April 1983.   (Eric Tonks)

Adderbury Quarries. Part of the quarried site was later occupied by Banbury Buildings Ltd, and the bases of the kilns were on their premises. This view of 28th September 1969 shows them across the then disused BR line. Kings Sutton church spire in the background.   (A. Donaldson)

nearby. He does not recall a locomotive at this period, so possibly it had been sold, and horses only used.

Of the 1859 tramway there are understandably no traces at all, nor of the canal wharf; the Chipping Norton line cut across the quarry, and the part to the north of the railway was first extended as part of the Sydenham Farm system and later built on by the Banbury Buildings complex. A small piece of the quarry extended south of the railway and there is still a slight dip by the railway fence, but the site of the tramway has been ploughed out.

There are much better traces of the later tramway system, considering the length of time since closure — more than three quarters of a century. The mound behind the Down platform at Kings Sutton station, and its relevance to the supposed ropeway, has been mentioned, and there is no trace apart from stonework on both banks of the river, of the bridge or of the line between station and canal; but west of the latter the tramway embankment is very clear. It ends abruptly about 40 yards from the bank and there is no trace of the line

Adderbury Quarries. There was a stiffish gradient from the quarries down to the canal and a small locomotive (so far unidentified) was used to haul empty wagons up and probably hold them on the way down. Our photograph of 7th February 1970 shows the former locomotive shed (demolished 1981). The tramway crossed the canal at the site of the lifting bridge shown, then the Cherwell — denoted by the pollard willows in the middle distance — to the GWR at Kings Sutton. The imposing spire of Kings Sutton church can be seen in the background.   (A. Donaldson)

down to the wharf, though some rotting piles in the bank probably come from it. The bridge over the canal is probably a modern replacement of similar design to the original. Be warned though; these bridges are kept 'open' almost permanently in these days of numerous pleasure craft, and the nearest crossing of the canal is at Kings Sutton lock; indeed, the canal is a greater barrier today than in Hickman's time. The simplest approach to the west side is from the Buckingham road. As the earthworks diminish at higher ground level the course of the line to the stone locomotive shed can be made out, and in the opposite direction another branch is revealed by flattening of the 'ridge and furrow'. Of the northern branch to the weighbridge there is no trace apart from a lowering of the land beyond the bridleway near the terminus. The locomotive shed, sorry to say, was demolished in 1981 and is now marked only by a pile of rough stone blocks surrounding a hollow (? an inspection pit). Beyond the locomotive shed area the tramway disappears, the ground having been disturbed again by the Sydenham Quarries described next. Of the level crossing over

Adderbury Quarries. Adderbury Ironstone Co quarried over a wide area on the west side of the Buckingham road, including ground north of the trackway to Bo Peep Farm. The tunnel beneath this was filled with concrete blocks, as shown here on 1st June 1975. (A. Donaldson)

the Buckingham road there is no trace, but on the western side there is plenty of evidence in the sunken fields, including the little spinney and the fields both sides. The drive to Bo Peep Farm is elevated all the way from the Buckingham road, leaving a well-defined face on the south side and, about half way along, the tunnel leading to the further quarrying area to the north. This tunnel consists of ironstone blocks with three rows of brick on top of the arch, and has been filled in beneath with concrete blocks; quite an impressive structure. In the north field a dip in the replacement hedge shows the extent of working and there are two replacement hedges crossing the south field. After eighty plus years, quite worth seeing.

Footnotes

1. Hugh Compton, letter 1st June 1983
2. Privately printed in Birmingham, 1913. I am indebted to the Religious Society of Friends for permission to inspect their copy.
3. *The Development of Corby Works* by (Sir) Frederick Scopes. Stewarts & Lloyds, 1968

Grid References

489391	Canal wharf—Railton tramway
493358	Bridge over Cherwell
492358	Bridge over canal
491357	Terminus of tramway west of canal
490357	Locomotive shed
481355	Bridge under track to Bo Peep Farm
495354	Canal wharf for shipment to Chipping Norton branch

Locomotive

Gauge: 2ft. 1in.(?)

—	0-4-0T OC	?	?	s/s c.1900

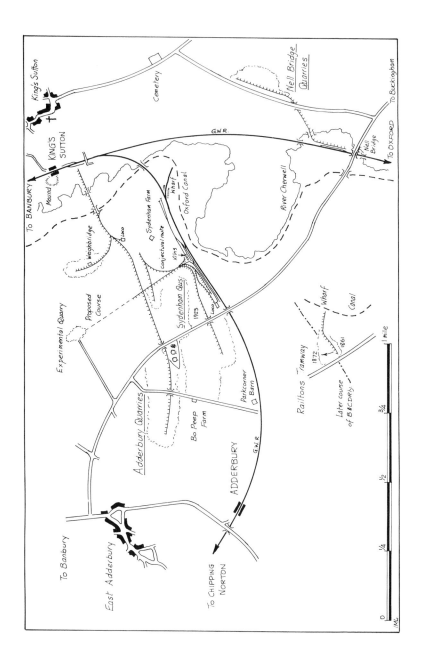

SYDENHAM QUARRIES

Owners: Alfred Hickman Ltd; Stewarts & Lloyds Ltd from April 1925.

This was a small compact system so named for its situation on land attached to Sydenham Farm that lay half a mile southeast of Kings Sutton church, on the high ground bounded by a loop in the Oxford canal. This ground lay between the two areas operated by Adderbury Ironstone Co and their successors Alfred Hickman Ltd, to the west and to the north, and which had been abandoned about the turn of the century. Details of the lease have not been discovered, but it would appear to have been far more extensive than the area that came to be worked; GSM states that the area was nearly 300 acres, and a map surviving among the documents at Bilston steelworks showed land at East End, East Adderbury, mostly north of the Buckingham road, but with a small area on the south side, by the fishponds, owned by or leased to Alfred Hickman. Most of the high ground between East Adderbury and the canal seems to have been acquired.

According to GSM, the property was opened up in March 1914 and by August 1917 had been rapidly developed, doubtless accelerated by wartime pressure. An account written by a visitor during the construction period[1] throws a most interesting light on the original plans, not elsewhere recorded as far as is known. The design of the kilns, then under construction, was based on those at Astrop, but modified by the Manager, Mr J. R. Owen, from the experience gained when he was manager at Astrop[2]. These were 'intended for dealing with the output of neighbouring mines. Trams conveying ore are to be run on the standard canal barges of the district close to the mines, and conveyed by water close to the calcining plant for discharging. They will then be taken to a vertical hoist for tipping into the kilns. Clearance of existing trams on the barges are very small—only 3in. between two rows of trams and 1½in. between trams and the side of the barge ... ore will be discharged directly into railway wagons by chutes distributed round the diameter of the kilns'.

The 'neighbouring mines' presumably refer to Adderbury (since at Astrop the GWR provided the far more convenient route, lying between the quarries and canal) and to Hickman's earlier tramway, wagons included, disused since about 1900; such a roundabout route

Sydenham Quarries. GERTRUDE seems never to have been photographed on site, but the picture is taken not far away — Neville's Garage at Chipping Norton in the early 1960's by Maurice Billington. She was later privately preserved.

could surely only have been considered because the facilities already existed. One difference will be noted; the ore was to be transported by barge, still in the tubs. This clumsy method, involving crossing the Chipping Norton branch to the kilns on the north side, was not adopted (and, but for Barrett's report, we confess, we would never have known of it) and a new 2ft-gauge tramway was laid down direct from quarries to kilns alongside the north side of Sydenham Sidings, 150 yards from the farm. The equipment and layout was very similar to that at Astrop, except that the tubs had to be raised mechanically to the tops of the kilns; they were run into the cage of a hoist, operated by a steam engine at the rear, and at the top were run along a gallery and then across the tops of the five kilns, each of which had a tippler at the mouth. The hoist was a double one, one cage travelling up while the other came down. After the ore was calcined, it was run directly into railway wagons for conveyance to Springvale Furnaces.

Another difference from Astrop was the use of steam locomotives on the tramway; the stock was munificent for so small a tramway—four locomotives—but these were purchased with expectations of working much further, up to three quarters of a mile from Sydenham Sidings. Three of the locomotives were neat little six-coupled side tanks supplied by Andrew Barclay; they were basically similar but differed in small details, as industrial locomotives will. They are recalled as having balloon spark arresters at first, and an official photograph of *Gertrude* shows her so fitted; but another photograph[3] shows *Winifred* without spark arrester, simpler lining and a whistle on the spectacle plate instead of the cab roof. In later years *Gertrude* had the whistle on the spectacle plate also, so perhaps there had been some rebuilding. The

Sydenham Quarries. Several of the older quarries in the Banbury area calcined their ore in kilns, a practice confined to the Oxfordshire Field. The set at Sydenham was of the Gyers type. Note the hoist to take the narrow gauge tubs to the tipplers on top of the kilns, and traces of the standard gauge siding in the foreground. Photographed by James Friswell and Son Ltd during demolition about 1932.

spark arresters made it difficult to get up steam in the mornings and they were soon discarded. The Barclays were painted green, lined black and white, it is believed, with the names transferred on to the tanks. *Margaret* and *Gertrude* were the names of the daughters of the Manager, Mr J. R. Owen, it is said, but one of the drivers also had a daughter Gertrude. The 4-6-0T was one of many built for war service by the Hunslet Engine Co, and several found service in quarry work in various parts of the country; but they had a proclivity for derailment—certainly at Sydenham, anyway—and *Margaret* was disposed of before long. The locomotive shed and offices were on ground excavated by their predecessors, adjoining the Buckingham road.

A 20 ton steam navvy was purchased from Ruston Proctor in 1915 but seems not to have been an unqualified success because of the amount of 'rubbish' taken up at the same time; as a result, hand operation that was first used was always practised to some extent, as noted in GSM; however, a further 20 ton navvy was bought in 1920. Working was northward from the outcrop; west of the farm the main tramway ran north-north-west from the kilns, with branches to east and west, the western side probably being developed first from the old Adderbury Ironstone face; after 1920 this branch was taken under the Buckingham road and the large field known as 'Navy Pit Ground' on the west side worked. As the working faces moved northwards the overburden increased, though it was never more than about ten feet; and the feature of step faulting (or 'dip and fault') was encountered.

As already stated, full development of the leased area was never realised. According to LI, the last operation seems to have been the driving of a gullet 400 yards in length in a northerly direction from the working face; this stopped short of a large area of stone under shallow cover, but nothing further was done, as the iron and steel industry was in a very depressed state. Further, by this time, Alfred Hickman Ltd had obtained leases for large tracts of land in the district served by Oxfordshire Ironstone Co Ltd, in which company they obtained a 50 per cent interest. As a result, their ironstone properties at Astrop and Sydenham were shut down, though the Sydenham reserves were known to be of the order of four million tons (Sir Frederick Scopes—letter 16th March 1966). At that time only two calcining kilns were apparently operating at Sydenham, not enough capacity to calcine the required output. The quarries at Sydenham were closed from June 1925 (*Banbury Guardian,* 11th June 1925); their first digger went to Oxfordshire Ironstone some time after 1925, and as the latter had a digger named *Jimmy*, it came as no surprise to learn that the new arrival was christened *Syd*! The remaining locomotives probably went about the same time, though the date is not known exactly. The track was lifted, but the kilns were left standing, as were the other buildings, including the locomotive shed; the kilns and associated equipment were dismantled, primarily for the metal work, by James Friswell & Sons Ltd, of Banbury, about 1932.

After World War II part of the site, including the buildings, was taken over by Portable Concrete Buildings Ltd, which became better known later as Banbury Buildings Ltd; the bases of the kilns—ironstone blocks and some brickwork—are still visible on their premises. The deserted shell of Sydenham Farm was later repaired and extended to

Sydenham Quarries. The geological formation of 'step faulting', with the layers displaced from the horizontal, is met with in a few quarries. This view shows the feature in the deserted quarry in May 1949. (B.G.S.)

form a group of farm buildings, and from it a bridleway runs to the Buckingham road, about half way along going up a sharp rise that denotes the limit of westward working. Parallel to the bridleway is a long terminal gullet running east-west; the ironstone 'bench' is very clearly preserved but shows no signs of the 'dip and fault' structure. The floor of the pit is coloured a deep red indicative of calcining, and the eastern end of the gullet is being filled in with rubbish in a desultory way. Of the 'experimental' gullet mentioned above, which was never opened out fully, traces of the north end can be seen in the long field northeast of the road at East End. The field on the west side of the Buckingham road shows clear signs of having been worked by its low level and the faces along the hedges; the tunnel under the road has been filled in but some of the stonework can still be seen, while on the east side the ground has been built upon. Two of the locomotives, *Gertrude* and *The Doll*, are, happily, preserved each after a rather chequered history.

The whole area was the subject of an application in April 1957 by Dowsett Mineral Recovery Ltd for planning permission to resume quarrying, along with another area at Bloxham. It was estimated that there remained 1.8 million tons of ore on the 185 acre site, and it was planned to remove this over a period of six to eight years; not more than 20 acres at a time would be out of cultivation, and lorry transport would be used to a railway siding, presumably close to the original Sydenham Farm connection. This came to nothing however (see under 'North Oxfordshire Ironstone Scheme').

Footnotes

1. Richard Thomas & Baldwins Ltd, Irthlingborough files, in BSC Archives. *Inspection of calcining kilns*. Report 10th September 1915. M. Barrett.
2. *Banbury Guardian*, 25th March 1915.
3. *Locomotive Magazine Souvenir No. 28*: Andrew Barclay Locomotives.

Grid References

490353	Junction with GWR
489353	Kilns
487352	Locomotive shed
491355	Sydenham Farm
488355	Terminal gullet—east end
487355	Terminal gullet—west end
485360	Experimental gullet—north end
486352	Bridge under Buckingham road

Locomotives

Gauge; 2ft. 0in.

WINIFRED	0-6-0T	OC AB	1424 1915	7 x 14in.	2ft. 2½in.	New 10/1915	(1)
GERTRUDE	0-6-0T	OC AB	1578 1918	7 x 14in.	2ft. 2½in.	New 4/1918	(1)
THE DOLL	0-6-0T	OC AB	1641 1919	7 x 14in.	2ft. 2½in.	New 8/1919	(1)
MARGARET	4-6-0T	OC HE	1324 1918	9½ x 12in.	2ft. 0in.	(a)	s/s

(a) ex-War Department, Railway Operating Department, c.1920.

(1) to Springvale Furnaces, Bilston, Staffordshire c.1926.

Quarry Machines

No. 20 S. Navvy	RP 429 1915			New 4/1915 (1)	
No. 20 S. Shovel	RH 576 1916	2¾ Cu.Yds.	31ft.	New 6/1920 s/s	

(1) to Oxfordshire Ironstone Co Ltd c.1926.

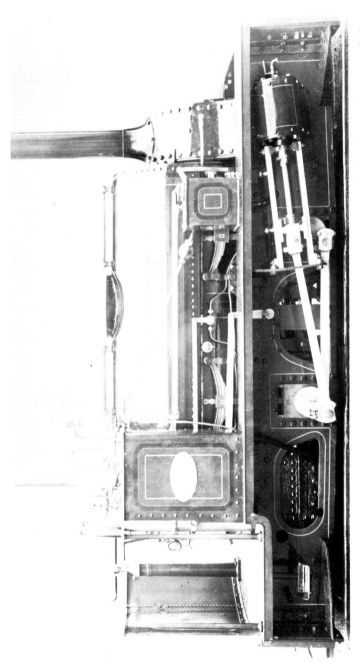

Adderbury Quarries. Locomotive operation on the 20-inch gauge tramway was short-lived, the inclined section of the tramway being changed to cable operation and the quarry lines worked by horses. However, the locomotive FLORENCE was an unusual one, as this official Manning Wardle photograph shows.

ADDERBURY QUARRIES

Owners: Hook Norton Ironstone Partnership; Cochrane & Co (Woodside) Ltd from about 1906; Duffield Iron Corporation from October 1928.

The Banbury and Cheltenham Direct Railway, promoted in 1874, was a revival of proposals to link the two towns and it was confidently expected that the line would not only enable the local ironstone deposits to be developed by making them accessible by rail to the Midlands but also provide a direct outlet to South Wales. At that time the only quarries being worked in the district were at East Adderbury, connected by tramway to the GWR main line and to the Oxford Canal. Financial difficulties delayed the completion of the line through Adderbury, which was opened for traffic 6th April 1887; and the Hook Norton Ironstone Partnership, formed to open up quarries at Hook Norton, also obtained leases to work ironstone on the south side of Adderbury station.

In March 1890 a series of trial holes were made at Park Farm, on the estate of William Chamberlain and, with a favourable report on the samples, a lease of the farm was negotiated with Mr. Chamberlain by a Mr. O. J. Williams of Westminster for a period of 21 years, the lease being dated 20th February 1890. Park Farm was put up for sale when Mr. Chamberlain died shortly afterwards, and the above details are taken from a copy of the sale catalogue (dated 22nd July 1891) now in the possession of Mr. J. J. Fox. We have no information on Mr. Williams but there can hardly be any doubt that this was the ground worked by the partnership. The map that accompanied the sale catalogue is unfortunately missing, and the area leased is not stated, but the farm buildings were excluded along with three fields, two of them ('Park Corner' and 'Great Ground') having 'an open ironstone pit' not being worked at the time; this would be part of the Adderbury Ironstone Co's ground, north of the railway.

Hook Norton Ironstone Partnership appear to have started operations in 1890, in which year they acquired their only known locomotive, *Florence*, of the unusual gauge of 1ft. 8in., and it seems likely that the tramway gauge was selected to suit the engine. The tramway commenced at a tipping dock alongside a railway siding in the station yard and then ran southwest, ascending the bank and passing beneath the bridleway to Paper Mill Cottages, to reach the working face on the eastern side of the Banbury-Oxford road. The incline had a gradient of approximately 1 in 17, hence the locomotive, which was a rather unusual Manning Wardle with a tall chimney and tapering safety valve cover but no cab; originally she conveyed coal from the Duke of Sutherland's colliery at Brora in Sutherland to the Highland Railway goods yard and in 1890 was offered for sale at Florence Colliery, Staffordshire, though it is unknown if she worked there. The colliery was owned by the Duke and the name *Florence* is one frequently associated with him.

The locomotive shed was at the top of the incline, as were the offices. Wagons were side-tippers, some of wood, with one side of the body hinged at the top so that it would swing clear when the body was tipped, and some v-shaped, holding about 15 cwt of ore. Locomotive operation was not entirely successful — possibly the gradient was too severe — and it was decided to work the main incline by cable with a stationary steam engine at the top, the line remaining single; traffic between summit and quarry face was worked by horses, *Florence* being despatched to Hook Norton where she could more usefully be employed.

The year when output commenced is not known; the first mention in LQ is for 1895, but as the quarries were shallow they may have escaped mention on that account. LQ then gives the quarries as 'standing' in 1896 and does not mention them again; but working recommenced at the end of May 1901 and continued at least through Christmas of that year (see *Banbury Guardian* 6th June and 26th December 1901). In 1903 the Partnership went into liquidation and shortly afterwards their Adderbury properties were taken over by Cochrane & Co (Woodside) Ltd, the proprietors of Woodside Ironworks at Dudley, who continued working between the bridleway and the Oxford road and also opened up two new areas. The first was a quarry west of the Oxford road, Berryhill Pit, to which access was gained via a bridge beneath the road; the incline to this pit was a funicular, i.e. double track. The second was New College Pit, also west of the main road but further south, and connected with the upper level by a tunnel and again worked by horses. New College, Oxford, was one of the principal landowners of the district and in this case possibly the lessor. The living of Adderbury Church is in the gift of New College.

It is not known precisely when the quarries were reopened by Cochrane's but they are quoted in Kelly's Directory from 1911 onwards, and in GSM as in being in 1914. They were worked until 1922, when the postwar slump in the British iron industry brought about the end of Woodside Ironworks. The 1923 6in. OS therefore shows the tramway system at its final and fullest extent.

While the quarries were at their busiest in the war years, the Brymbo Steel Co Ltd were hovering in the background, seeking an opportunity to enter the area; they were already well established at Hook Norton and either had, or were negotiating for, a 40-year lease of Ecclesiastical Commissioner's land between Bloxham and Milton. Mr. J. J. Fox kindly provided this information and also let us see letters discovered by the Adderbury History Group; these were written by Brymbo in the period September 1916 to January 1917 and from them it appears that the company were negotiating for leases on ground adjacent to all three of Cochrane's pits. That near New College Pit included Bellows Covert and Blackingrove Farm; the accompanying map has not survived but the proposed term of 60 years from 25th March 1917 implies a considerable area. Just how Brymbo proposed to get their ore to the railway without using Cochrane's tramway is not clear, as the offer for leases make no mention of Cochrane's at all. However, this speculation is academic, as there is no evidence of any of the leases being concluded or the ground worked.

Returning to practicalities, Cochrane's plants at Woodside and Adderbury were offered for sale and in the advertisement in the *Manchester Guardian* of 10th May 1924 the tramway gauge is given as 2ft.—evidently an error for 20in., as all other sources have the gauge as 1ft. 8in. throughout. Hopes that the Wingerworth Iron Co might reopen the quarries were dashed by the 1926 General Strike, but a partial revival came about in October 1928 when the Duffield Iron Corporation, a firm of consulting engineers that had been formed the previous February, acquired the site in order to carry out work on a patent method of iron ore reduction by pulverised coal. A furnace was erected and a hand-fed calcinating kiln, while a Hudson 'go-go' tractor was purchased to bring wagons of ore down the tramway to the plant. This locomotive had a 20hp Fordson engine, central spring buffers and a steel canopy; we are indebted to Andrew Neale for this information.

The plant continued to operate in a small way up to the outbreak of war, when the owners pressed the Ministry of Supply to support their developments, as part of the War Effort. In 1940 a small delegation formed at the request of the Iron & Steel Controller, visited and reported on the Duffield plant. This report was unfavourable to Duffield and, following it, the Ministry of Aircraft Production, with the

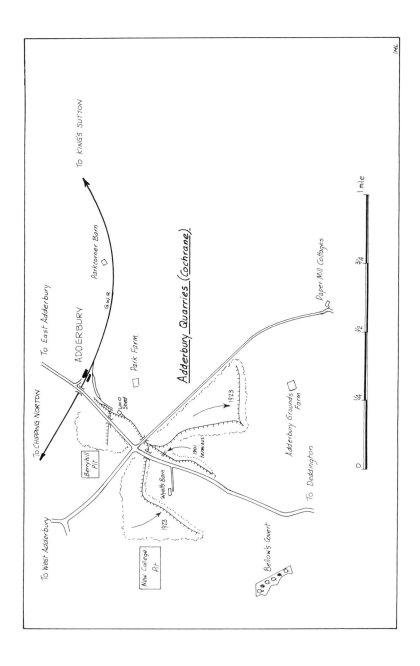

To KING'S SUTTON

Parkcorner Barn

G.W.R.

To East Adderbury

ADDERBURY

Park Farm.

To CHIPPING NORTON

Loco Shed

Berryhill Pit

To West Adderbury

Watts Barn

1923

1923

New College Pit

1901 Terminus

Adderbury Grounds Farm

To Deddington

Bellow's Covert

Paper Mill Cottages

Adderbury Quarries (Cochrane).

0   ¼   ½   ¾   1 mile

IML

approval of the Ministry of Supply, sponsored the use of the site by Northern Aluminium Co Ltd. We are indebted to Sir Frederick Scopes for this information; he was a member of the delegation in his capacity of Director of Home Ore. The tramway was dismantled and the lower portions of the site levelled and covered by buildings that after the war were taken over and extended by the Twyford Seed Factory.

The lower part of the tramway route has disappeared completely and of the upper portions there is very little to be seen, while the quarries themselves were too shallow to leave much of a mark on the land. The tramway bridge under the bridleway has disappeared without trace but the terminal face of the eastern quarry to the south remains; this was the largest of the three quarried areas. A mound of earth on the east side of the Oxford road may possibly be a relic of quarrying, possibly not. There is no trace of the tunnel under the Oxford road to Berryhill Pit. The tunnel to New College Pit remained in being until the 1960s, with an ivy-covered fence atop the parapet on the west side. This last had gone by 1980, but there are gaps in the hedges on both sides of the road; the ground on each side has been levelled. The terminal face of New College Pit is, however, still extant at the back of Wyatt's Barn, a quarter-mile length facing away from the road, and the course of the tramway alongside it clearly defined. The 1923 6in. OS indicates that operations here only commenced at the next hedge to the west, and it is certainly the best preserved face, and worth seeing. A further quarter mile to the southwest, on the high ground overlooking Bellow's Covert, the ground has been disturbed but not, it seems, for quarrying, nor is there any trace of a tramway here.

Grid References

472347	Top of incline/locomotive shed
471346	Bridge under bridleway
472348	Bridge under Oxford road to Berryhill Pit
470345	Bridge under Oxford road to New College Pit
465343	Terminal face of New College Pit — south end

Locomotives

Hook Norton Ironstone Partnership
Gauge; 1ft. 8in.

FLORENCE   0-4-0ST   OC   MW   579   1875   6 x 8in.   1ft. 8in.   (a)   (1)

(a) ex Florence Coal and Iron Co Ltd, Trentham, Staffordshire, 1890.
(1) to Hook Norton Quarries 1892.

Duffield Iron Corporation Ltd
Gauge; 1ft. 8in.

               4 w P M   Hu   36777   1929   20hp   New 7/1929   S/s

Bloxham to Hook Norton

The potential for ironstone traffic on the Banbury and Cheltenham
Direct Railway had been recognised from its promotion in 1874 and
plans were being formulated in advance of its arrival on 6th April 1887.
The new line facilitated developments at Adderbury, as we have seen,
while Hook Norton was opened up within two years. At Bloxham
station the Oxfordshire Ironstone Co Ltd (no relation to the wellknown
company operating around Wroxton from 1919) started preparatory
work in the 1880s but these were not pursued and it was not until
World War I that the ironstone was worked here, by two separate
companies. At Hook Norton, early development was encouraged by
the outcrop of stone close to the station and on the sides of the valleys
crossed by the two fine viaducts to the south; in the early years of the
century four operators were at work, and it is interesting to see how
they tackled the common problem of the difficult contours. By the end
of World War I only Brymbo was still working and they carried on until
the end of World War II. Fortunately for us, the area has been very
thoroughly researched by the Hook Norton Local History Group. In the
1960s there were plans for the future development of the whole district
on a scale so great that the local population were stirred into protest
similar to that attending the 'Third London Airport', and the plan was
dropped; but the Banbury people retail stories of the conflict to this
day.

BLOXHAM QUARRIES

**Owners: Bloxham Ironstone Co Ltd: Bloxham & Whiston
Ironstone Co Ltd from 27th December 1917**

These quarries and the ones described later both referred to in all
official sources as 'Bloxham Quarries', were opened in 1918 as a result
of wartime drive, the present ones being the earlier by a few months.
The prime mover and original lessee was Alfred Wassall, who joined

forces with two directors of Islip Iron Co Ltd, P. R. LeMare and A. C. J. Wall, to form Bloxham Ironstone Co Ltd, registered 16th February 1916; Islip's managing director, N. W. Kidner, joined the board in September. To this company King's College, Eton, granted a lease of Oldbarn Farm and Wayhouse Farm, comprising 275 acres north of Milton village, as from 29th September 1916, and renewable on a yearly basis; this lease superseded an Indenture with Alfred Wassell made 14th December 1915.

Islip's involvement seems to have been purely proprietorial, as Islip Works were adequately supplied from quarries in their immediate vicinity; the Bloxham ore went principally to Staffordshire and South Wales, the traditional markets for Oxfordshire ore. This was despatched via a standard gauge tramway that connected with the western end of a set of three sidings provided by the GWR half a mile west of Milton Halt. The tramway was built by Caffin & Co Ltd, the well-known railway contractors, and was a very substantial affair of its kind. Immediately after leaving the GWR sidings the line curved north in a broad cutting some 20ft. deep and then on a high embankment over a stream; a short and shallow cutting brought the line to the south of Oldbarn Farm and the north-south working face a third of a mile long. The well-laid track was spiked throughout but later the main line was chaired with plate-chairs designed to accommodate the flat-bottomed rail; spiked rail sufficed for the pits, for ease of slewing. The original locomotive shed was of wood and is believed to have stood at the north end of the embankment over the stream, where the ground was level; but it was soon replaced by a more substantial structure of brick at the marshalling sidings. This shed was constructed by David Clifton of Bloxham, whose family had been builders and masons for many years; it had one road with accommodation for machinery at the side, and the rear end was arched so that a straight-through line could easily be constructed if desired by knocking out the bricks under the arch. Water was obtained from the brook between junction and pits, being pumped into a reservoir by the locomotive shed and into a tank at the pits; the tank is still in use for the convenience of Oldbarn Farm, the former spring feeding the farm having been destroyed by quarrying operations.

For the most part, only light cover of some five feet of Upper Lias clay had to be dealt with and the ground was level, so the working conditions were good—though the stone was said to be somewhat limey. A trial load of ore was despatched to Birchill's Furnaces in

February 1917, Caffins doing the loading, and regular production is first recorded in the board minutes for February 1918. By this time the company title had changed to Bloxham & Whiston Ironstone Co Ltd with the acquisition of the Whiston quarries near Castle Ashby, also owned by Wassell. At Bloxham three more leases—Arthur Stockton (36½ acres); T. H. Hawkes (19 acres); and Miss F. Malsbury (143 acres)—extended their holdings from the Eton College ground as far west as the Bloxham-Banbury road, and north to the Soar Brook. These were all backdated for a term of 26 years from 29th September 1917, and a royalty of 3d per ton was imposed. The whole of the leased area, Eton College included, was part of the Broughton Estate, and the leases carried the approval of Lady Saye & Sele.

Two 20-ton steam diggers were obtained new from Ruston & Hornsby, the first in February 1918, when regular production

Bloxham Quarries (B & W). Bloxham & Whiston Ironstone Co Ltd had two 20-ton Ruston & Hornsby shovels in the quarries. Our photograph shows one of them, taken by Mr Purser about 1923, and given to Mr Parrot, the driver. One of these machines, possibly both, went to Islip Quarries in Northamptonshire.   (J. J. Fox Collection)

Bloxham Quarries (B & W). These quarries closed in 1929, too early to attract the attentions of industrial locomotive photographers. However, BETTY and MARGÔT (named respectively after the daughters of directors Norman Kidner and A. C. J. Wall) served for many years at Islip Ironworks and elsewhere. This photograph of BETTY was taken at Buckminster Quarries, Lincolnshire, 11th March 1961. (K. Cooper/IRS Collection)

commenced; the ore was loaded directly into 12- and 15-ton railway wagons supplied by the Ministry of Munitions. The latter body also authorised the employment of 30 German prisoners-of-war from the Banbury Camp, who worked from April 1918 until the end of May 1919; at first their efforts were poorly regarded, but improved with time—after all, they may have been used to very different work in civilian life. To accommodate new local labour some houses were built at Milton in 1919-20.

The contractors had two six-coupled Hunslet locomotives on the job, *Mersey* and *Barry*, and the latter was taken over together with three wagons by the quarry company when production commenced. Two new locomotives were ordered, an Avonside and a Peckett, the latter arriving in September 1918 and the Avonside in December. Some mystery surrounds the latter engine, which was immediately offered for sale without apparently ever having turned a wheel in service. The opinion was later expressed that with her steel firebox and tubes she could not stand up to the work—but there just does not seem to have been time for anyone to find out her capabilities! She was sold, as was *Barry*, in February 1919, and another Peckett ordered. The earlier Peckett, *Margôt*, was so named after the elder daughter of A. C. J. Hall, and had one of the very few nameplates to sport a circumflex; sister loco *Betty* was named after Norman Kidner's daughter. Their livery is uncertain: the real Margôt, from a childhood footplate trip, described *Margôt* as 'a great big black engine'. We are indebted to her sister, Miss Catherine Wall, for these reminiscences. These two locomotives handled the whole of the quarry's subsequent output, which averaged about 10,000 tons per year; calcining was practised on a small scale, but no kilns were built, though mooted in 1919.

From 28th January 1920 the company, along with Islip Iron Co Ltd, became a subsidiary of Drayton Iron & Steel Co Ltd. This latter company was associated with the wagon-building firm of S. J. Claye Ltd, of Long Eaton, and the first act of the board afterwards was to purchase new wagons, as well as to hire some from the Ministry of Munitions, who were relinquishing control of the industry. Some of the wagons were 20-ton hoppers, the rest standard 10 and 12 tonners, according to Mr Flint, a former employee. They were painted lead colour with *Drayton* in white on the sides. Some of the wagons were supplied by S. J. Claye, others by Stableford of Coalville. Just after a batch had been delivered, a derailment occurred when they were being propelled up to the pits in the usual way; the leading wagon jumped the rails and plunged over the embankment, the others following to form an untidy heap by the brook. A long weekend of hard work, including the laying of a ramp down the embankment, was required to get the wagons back on the road.

The postwar drop in demand brought about the closure of the quarries in 1921 but they were reopened on a part-time employment basis and in this uncertain condition carried on. The board minutes of Islip Iron Co Ltd from September 1924 onwards lists 'wagon journeys' at their various plants, including Bloxham, recording an output rising from 1924 to 1926, then dramatically falling in 1927, with the last movements in June of that year. From these records it seems that this was the effective end of activity here but the quarries were not offically closed until October 1929. The two locomotives were transferred to

Islip Ironworks and, of the two diggers, one definitely went to Islip quarries for work, the other probably also, but in a dismantled state. The track at Bloxham was taken up a few years after the closure and some of it went to Oxfordshire Ironstone Co Ltd. A few lengths of track remained in the marshalling yard by the GWR line as "no one knew if it belonged to the GWR or to the ironstone company", as one railway man described it to John Batts.

There are plenty of remains to be seen. The trackbed is intact all the way from the BR sidings area to Oldbarn Farm and the cutting is indeed used by lorries from the direction of Milton, travelling a distance along the BR trackbed first. But the most interesting exhibit is undoubtedly the locomotive shed, which was well built and probably less than ten years old at the closure, and was used for storing agricultural machinery. It was so used thirty years after the closure, still in good condition and an impressive memorial to the builder. Sad to say, this is no longer the case; but we can describe the building as it was—and is—for the record. It is of red brick with seven buttressed brickwork pillars each side and six round-topped steel-framed windows. There are two steel crosspieces in the roof. As mentioned above, the rear end was arched, and the bricks were knocked out at some time in the 1960s, but a straight wooden lintel set in and the space above filled with brick to give a squarish doorway below. At the front end there is a runner for a sliding door, presumably the original fitting. There was one 'pot' between the fourth and fifth buttresses. In the early 1970s use of the shed by the occupier had ceased and by 1975 most of the roof had gone—possibly by fire—and the building surrounded by trees and invaded also by them; though the 'pot' was still in position.

Other buildings in the yard were also half buried in undergrowth. By 1985 the shed was still standing, more ruinous than ever, with severe cracks at the east end; the other buildings had all gone and the yard was being used as a rubbish tip, seemingly for items thrown out by the scrapyard up the Bloxham road—a sad end to what had been up to then a picturesque spot. The cutting towards the quarry area is however still much the same, and a pleasant walk it makes. The water tank remains at Oldbarn Farm and beyond this the ground falls away gently and in wet weather a sheet of water covers the sunken ground of the former quarried area to the west, which is crossed by a replacement fence. No quarrying took place other than on the Eton College land.

Bloxham Quarries (B & W). The locomotive shed, built by a local man, David Clifton, was the major exhibit to survive closure. and for many years was used by a farmer; but nature has taken its toll and demolition cannot be far off. This photograph was taken 14th March 1970, the site pinpointed by Bloxham church spire. GWR siding trackbed to left. (A. Donaldson)

In April 1957 Dowsett Mineral Recovery Ltd applied for planning permission to resume quarrying a much larger area here and at Adderbury. The 976-acre site was said to contain 17.5 million tons of ore, to be worked over a period of 30-35 years, with no more than 40 acres sterilized at a time; the ore would be conveyed by lorries, each holding 22 tons of ore, to rail sidings at Milton — evidently utilizing the existing trackbed. As reported in the *Banbury Guardian* of 17th July 1958, the landowners, Trinity College, Oxford, raised no objection, but permission was ultimately refused (see under 'North Oxfordshire Ironstone Scheme').

Grid References

445353	Junction with GWR
446353	Locomotive shed
448355	Cutting—north end
447359	Tank by Oldbarn Farm
445365	Terminal face—north end

Locomotives

Gauge; 4ft. 8½in.

BARRY	0-6-0ST	IC	HE	363	1885	13 x 18in.	3ft. 1in.	(a)	(1)
MARGÔT	0-6-0ST	OC	P	1456	1918	14 x 20in.	3ft. 7in.	New 9/1918	(2)
EDGAR	0-6-0ST	OC	AE	1815	1918	14 x 20in.	3ft. 3in.	New 12/1918	(3)
BETTY	0-6-0ST	OC	P	1549	1919	14 x 20in.	3ft. 7in.	New 11/1919	(4)

(a) ex Caffin & Co Ltd, contractors, 1917.

(1) to Rossington Main Colliery Co Ltd 4/1919.
(2) to Islip Ironworks 1929.
(3) to Skinningrove Iron Co Ltd, via War Dept. Disposals Board, Canterbury, c.1919.
(4) to Islip Ironworks 1931.

Quarry Machines

No. 20 S. Navvy	RH	500	1918	2¾ Cu.Yds.	31ft.	New 1/1918 s/s
No. 20 S. Navvy	RH	572	1919	2¾ Cu.Yds.	31ft.	New 10/1919 (1)

(1) to Islip Quarries c.1931

BLOXHAM QUARRIES

Owners: Northamptonshire Ironstone Co Ltd: Clay Cross Co Ltd from 25th December 1926.

In practical terms ironstone quarrying at Bloxham dates only from World War I but plans to work ironstone both here and at Hook Norton were in existence in the middle 1880s, some three or four years before the opening of the Banbury & Cheltenham Direct Railway, construction of which had been suspended since 1877 because of financial difficulties. It was doubtless in hopes of early completion of the line that the quarry interests made their plans; and possibly because of the delays that they made so little practical progress — none

Bloxham Quarries (Clay Cross). These quarries were started by J. W. Pain under the title Northamptonshire Ironstone Co Ltd, but saw little activity until Clay Cross Co Ltd took over. The Peckett steam locomotive NORTHFIELD worked the traffic until the early 1930s, when she was replaced by a petrol-electric machine. She is here shown out of use at the station siding 31st July 1933.   (J. P. Mullett)

at all at Bloxham and only for a comparatively short time at Hook Norton. Nevertheless, the negotiations are not without interest, and the titles of the companies anticipated later developments.

Ground on both sides of the trackbed of the railway at Bloxham station was purchased in February 1883 by the Oxfordshire Ironstone Co Ltd (registered 4th April 1882), and in the following year passed to the Bloxham Ironstone Co Ltd, who leased it to Hook Norton Ironstone Partnership Ltd for 21 years from 1st May 1889, with the low royalty of 2d per ton of ore. There were a number of mortgages raised in connection with these transfers of land. Nothing further was done at the time but the freehold of the ground north of the railway was later acquired by James Pain. Allusion has already been made to the Pain family history, and its influence on the ironstone industry; just before World War I, J. W. Pain left the parent company and set up in business on his own account in a number of scattered localities, of which Bloxham was one; his younger brother, Lance, was here for a time. James Pain lived at Whiston Hall then. It is rather curious that while James Pain's Whiston Quarries were taken over by Bloxham & Whiston Ironstone Co Ltd, his Bloxham quarries were not, but came under Clay Cross, as Bloxham & Whiston Ironstone Co Ltd had already commenced operations at their own Bloxham pits (see previous section).

In addition to the freehold property already mentioned, Pain negotiated two leases, the first and more important being with Samuel Lamley Fisher of Grimston Hall, Banbury, for 40 years from 29th September 1917. The area of about 150 acres lay east of the village between the stream (south) and the Tadmarton road (north) and between the freehold area (east) and the parish boundary (west), plus one field north of the Tadmarton road. The royalty was set at 4d per ton. The second lease was with 'The President of the College Royal of the Blessed Mary of Eton, commonly called The King's College of our Blessed Lady of Eton'; this was for 40 years from 25th December 1919 and the royalty 3½d per long ton of 2,352lbs. The area of about 100 acres comprised part of Nayland Farm, one mile northwest of Bloxham church, and lying a third of a mile from the Tadmarton road, and therefore isolated from the other areas. Both these leases were transferred to Northamptonshire Ironstone Co Ltd as the nominal operators.

It seems that Pain's operations were confined to a small area immediately east of the village, adjoining Cumberford, and with the quarry so close the simplest of transport arrangments sufficed. A light standard gauge tramway was built from the GWR goods yard, a six-coupled Peckett saddle tank transferred from Byfield quarries to provide motive power, and a steam navvy to excavate a gullet, production commencing about September 1918; but the reduced demand of the postwar years brought about closure in the early 1920s, a date not recorded or remembered any more precisely. The Northamptonshire Ironstone Co Ltd was in liquidation in May 1925. The 6in. OS shows an apparent tramway formation north of the station that may have been used to work the small quarry here before the main quarry line was built—but if so, it would have been too short to require a locomotive. The ground here was certainly worked, however.

Early in 1927 (about February) the quarries were reopened by the Clay Cross Co Ltd, who took over the two leases cited for the remainder of the term, as from 25th December 1926. The company applied for, and received, an extension of time in respect of the Fisher lease, to 25th December 1960; but trade in the late 1920s was not sufficiently encouraging for them to open up the Nayland Farm area, the lease for which was determined as from 25th December 1929. The isolated field of the Fisher lease north of the main road was also never touched.

The tramway was extended about a third of a mile parallel to the Tadmarton road and ground on the south side worked in long strips. Clay Cross did not make any great changes in operating methods, and continued with hand filling that had been practiced since the navvy had opened up the initial gullet. The Peckett *Northfield* was the sole locomotive and when she required a retube a four-coupled saddle tank *Betty* was hired from an unknown source. The only information about her is that she was painted brown, while *Northfield* was green. About 1930, the boiler inspector imposed on *Northfield* a maximum pressure of 80lbs and she was withdrawn from service and eventually taken down to the GWR goods yard and scrapped there, where Mr J. P. Mullett photographed her in 1933. In replacement a petrol electric locomotive was supplied from Clay Cross Works; this and its better known successor *Amos* were rebuilds of 60cm gauge machines built by Nasmyth Wilson and other makers for the War Department about 1918, a number of which were purchased by Clay Cross.

The track was flat-bottomed on wooden sleepers, laid with a minimum of earthwork, as was James Pain's custom. Derailments were frequent, with *Northfield* because of her long wheelbase and with the

Bloxham Quarries (Clay Cross). During most of Clay Cross ownership, the quarries were served by petrol-electric locomotives rebuilt by Clay Cross from War Department machines. The one shown is the best known, AMOS, from the Ashover Light Railway, converted for running on standard gauge metals. She is here shown in the sidings at the station in September 1954, four months after closure, awaiting removal.

(Eric Tonks)

petrol locomotive because of its lightness (10 tons against *Northfield's* 32). There was a ramp of 1 in 30 between quarry and locomotive shed and on this the adhesion weight of the petrol locomotive was scarcely enough to hold the two loaded wagons (30 tons stone and 14 tons tare) that made up the normal train from the pits. The locomotive shed in later years consisted of a flat-roofed windowless erection of wood and corrugated iron, at the reversing point beyond the weighbridge; this would not have been suitable for *Northfield* in size or construction but details of any other shed are not recalled and there may not have been one, strange as it seems.

The Nayland Farm site was not opened up, as already stated, but in the Clay Cross records is an interesting map showing the proposed tramway connection; the existing line was to be extended alongside the Tadmarton road to a point just beyond the Hobb Hill turn, then crossing the road on the level and running towards the southwest corner of Nayland Farm lease, the most convenient access point. Had it materialized, this would have been a very attractive route, reminiscent of Charwelton and, with the 1 in 60 gradient in favour of the load, fairly easy to work; but it was not to be.

Work at Bloxham was hard; it was difficult to run trains without mishap on the tramway, while in the quarry hand operation was in force up to 1942, making Bloxham the last ironstone qurry of consequence to be so worked. In the earlier days when about a dozen men were employed, each did his own drilling at ¾d per foot and received 8/9d for filling a 15-ton wagon; 36/- was considered a good week's pay and wet days, Bank Holidays etc were just lost days. This drudgery terminated in 1942 when all the men were transferred temporarily to Wroxton; "which was the best thing that ever happened; it was like going on holiday" said Edward Clarke, the genial factotum who joined the staff in March 1919 at the age of 17 and worked throughout the life of the quarry, and who has contributed largely to these notes, supplementing with his personal reminiscences the extensive records kept at Clay Cross.

The temporary closure on 28th February 1942 was imposed by the Ministry of Supply 'in the National Interest', a term that could be used to justify all sorts of unpleasant decisions but in this case was completely true. At that time ten men were employed and the output averaged about 500 tons per week; the better facilities at Oxfordshire Ironstone would undoubtedly show a great improvement on that, and Clay Cross protested in vain at the expensive re-equipping of "old and abandoned mines at Charwelton and Byfield" while at Bloxham there was a long face with small overburden. For the rest of the war Bloxham quarries lay silent and abandoned only from the point of view of ironstone production; the foreman, G. H. Sykes, was retained to keep an eye on things and from December 1943 to September 1944 the War Department used the quarry as a rifle range. Parts of the worked-out areas were ploughed up and utilized for food production.

When the war was over, the authorities seemed anxious to forget all about Bloxham, and one can sympathise with Clay Cross when they commenced negotiations in January 1946 to reopen the quarries; the M.O.S. refused any payment in compensation for damage, or help in clearing the undergrowth that had taken over much of the site. The employment of former Bloxham men by Oxfordshire Ironstone ceased at the end of July 1945, but the quarries were not reopened until the beginning of 1948; indeed it is quite likely that they would never have been reopened at all but for the impending closure of Clay Cross's other quarries at Brixworth where the reserves (and some of the equipment!) were nearing exhaustion. The 55RB electric dragline was transferred to Bloxham, which thus received at last a measure of mechanisation; even so, production in these later years was considerably lower than in the days of hand filling.

Operations seem to have been resumed at the face paralleling the Tadmarton road (last worked in 1942), continuing westward. To reach this the tramway did a full semicircle and to simplify access installation of an overhead cableway from the face to an unloading station near the tramway reversing point was considered, but this was not done. In January 1950 it was proposed to extend the tramway cutting to open a new face further west, but unfortunately the stone proved to be very poor, and efforts to lease new ground nearer the Tadmarton road beyond the Fisher lease came to nothing. The Tadmarton road face with its shallow overburden was therefore abandoned and the deeper Cumberford Hill face, formerly worked by James Pain, reopened. This is the reverse of normal ironstone history, where quarries progressively further away are worked.

On the tramway things were very much the same, as the locomotive supplied was of the same type as the last, an ex-World War I petrol-electric conversion. This one had an interesting history, though. She had worked on the Ashover Light Railway (owned by Clay Cross) and had been converted from the two foot gauge by mounting the engine on a wider frame with inside bearings to the wheels; she was painted plain black with the company title in white paint on the right-hand cab sheet, and the name in wooden letters screwed to the radiator front and in white paint on the rear. The name was bestowed more or less as a joke when the engine was on the ALR, where Amos Hinds was quarry manager[1].

The staff consisted of three men only; "the navvy driver (Tom Jones); one (Joe King) to do baring; while I (Ted Clarke) do the loco driving, office work and about forty other jobs". As a labour-saving device wagons were loaded in two stages, the lower half being filled at a face where the top layers of stone had been removed and then moved along to a more recently exposed face. This was easily the smallest setup of any ironstone system, and lends an added poignancy to the tragic death of one of the trio on 26th April 1953, when *Amos* was in the shed receiving attention to the axle boxes and suddenly plunged forward off the jacks, pinning the navvy driver beneath the cowcatcher and killing him.

It is surprising that the Bloxham quarries lasted as long as they did but it was evidently intended to work them until the lease expired in 1960, which would still have left much of the leased ground unworked. But things did not go that far and the imposition in March 1954 of increased freight charges by BR was just sufficient to make further working uneconomic because of the lengthy haul involved. The pits were closed on 15th May 1954 and the lease determined from 25th December 1960. A 'new diesel locomotive' was being built at the time at Clay Cross Works—actually another rebuild like *Amos* but with a diesel engine; the petrol machines were inordinately heavy on fuel consumption and the new machine could have been more economical. What happened to it is unknown.

The effects were purchased by Marple & Gillott Ltd, of Sheffield, for dismantling and the track was taken up, *Amos* being left at the end of the spur from the BR goods yard to await its fate; by September only a few electric cables were left. *Amos* was purchased by W. Bush & Sons Ltd of Alfreton, converted to diesel drive with a Gardner engine and fluid flywheel and sent in March 1955 by road to Helmdon to assist in the dismantling of the former SMJR Towcester-Cockley Brake line.

Late in 1958 came a possibility of revival by a company otherwise unconnected with the iron and steel industry, Robert MacGregor & Sons Ltd of Manchester. They had been operating opencast coal sites and because of the drop in this type of work they had spare equipment available. They acquired an interest in the area formerly operated by Clay Cross and proposed to reopen the workings in about six month's time[2], with an initial output of 3,000 tons per week, rising to 14,000 tons. They proposed to use dumpers on an internal road to the BR siding at Bloxham station—Clay Cross's former despatch point, in fact. Had this application been made in isolation, permission would probably have been granted, but it was swallowed up in the much bigger contemporary application by Dowsett Mineral Recovery Ltd (see under 'North Oxfordshire Ironstone Scheme'), and was refused. The site was said to comprise 100 acres, 25 of which had already been worked and 65 could be worked by MacGregors.

For some ten years after the closure, the course of the tramway was easily traceable, and the terminal face prominently visible from Cumberford Hill; the locomotive shed was demolished but the office remained. Since then however the area around the station has been developed as a housing estate and all traces on the ground obliterated; but at the end of Cumberford Close the terminal face is still very obvious, with an extra 'cut' at the southern end. The face can be followed round a smooth curve to the Tadmarton Road quarry, shallower there, but the sunken area denoting the former quarry can be recognised. Two hundred yards beyond Cumberford Close the workings are crossed by a farm track and northwest of this the tramway cutting is clearly visible and gradually diverging from the main quarried area; this presumably is the 1950 cutting made to open up ground further west, and it stretches some 150 yards beyond the Tadmarton Road quarry. Northeast of the terminus there is evidence of attempts at quarrying—again, presumably, the abortive efforts of 1950 that led to the abandonment of the site. The tramway cutting is still very clearly defined but has to be sought across the fields, being practically invisible from the road. The proposed course of the line to Nayland Farm can be explored as a public footpath, and while there is of course no evidence of anything being done, one can wonder how many wagons the locomotive could have held on the bank crossing the flank of Hobb Hill!

Footnotes

1. *The Ashover Light Railway.* I. Gotheridge & K. P. Plant. 1955, p.19
2. *BR (WR) Monthly Report to BTC*, January 1959.

Grid References

424354	Junction with GWR
425355	Terminus of early line
422354	Locomotive shed
419359	Terminal face—north end
424357	Face by Cumberford Close

Locomotives

Gauge; 4ft. 8½in.

NORTHFIELD	0-6-0ST	OC	P 717 1897		14 x 20in.	3ft. 7in.	(a)	Scr c. 1936
BETTY	0-4-0ST	OC	- ?				(b)	(1)
-		4WPE	Clay Cross c.1927				(c)	(2)
AMOS		4WPE	Clay Cross c.1928				(d)	(3)

(a) ex Byfield Quarries 1918.
(b) ex ?. hire.
(c) ex Clay Cross Works c.1930.
(d) ex Clay Cross Works 11/1947 (formerly on Ashover Light Railway).

(1) to ?, after hire.
(2) to Brixworth Quarries c.1942.
(3) to W. Bush & Sons Ltd, contractors, Helmdon, via Marple & Gillott Ltd, 3/1955.

Quarry Machines

S. Navvy   (a) s/s
55RB E. Dragline   RB 5100 1940   (b) s/s

(a) ex ?
(b) ex Brixworth Quarries c.1948

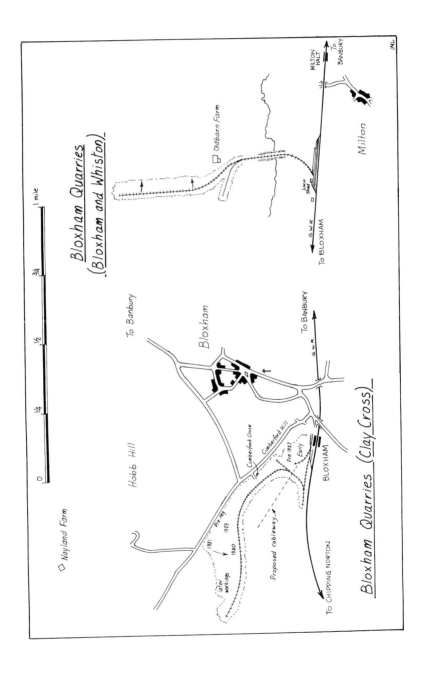

Bloxham Quarries
(Bloxham and Whiston)

Bloxham Quarries (Clay Cross)

GREAT TEW QUARRIES

Owner: M. E. Boulton

The only official reference to ironstone quarrying here is recorded in LQ for 1895 under the title 'Field Barn Quarry, Great Tew'; for 1896-1901 the quarry is described as 'standing' and thereafter appears no more. There are several quarries in the vicinity of Great Tew and LI states 'A rather large pit, overgrown by trees and called Chascombe Clump ... about 250 yards west-south-west of 'Ley's Field Barn' seems to be the most probable site ... no other quarry in Great Tew parish

Great Tew Quarry. Site of the former quarry in Chascombe Clump, 25th February 1981. This quarry only worked for about a year but is interesting for its association with the Boulton family, who played so important a part in the Industrial Revolution. (Eric Tonks)

appears likely to have been an ironstone working'. Field survey in February 1982 confirmed this view. The only other quarry of any consequence is at Quarry Green, 600 yards northwest of Court Farm, but this was 'clearly for building stone, not iron ore, and partly dressed blocks of stone still lie in it' (LQ, p.195). In 1982 there was a disused winch and a shed at the entrance where the stone was dressed.

Today Chescoombe Clump (the OS spelling) is a spinney of larches growing over an area that has been shallowly excavated, and the appearances suggest that quarrying was abandoned after a number of abortive attempts to obtain good quality ore. The 1886 and 1900 OS maps both show the Clump as having a mixture of deciduous and coniferous trees, with no indication of quarrying, but there seems no likelier site, and if this is the one, then the OS of 1900 was presumably copied from the earlier edition without detailed checks on site. The 'Big House' of Tew Park was the home of the Boulton family, and M. E. Boulton is recorded in the *Banbury Guardian* of 1st December 1870 as being brought home as a baby by his parents on 23rd November 1870, so would be only a young man at the time of the quarrying experiment. The great days of Tew Park are long past and the village of Great Tew a mixture of restored and neglected buildings.

Grid References

388303	Chescoombe Clump
390295	Stone quarry

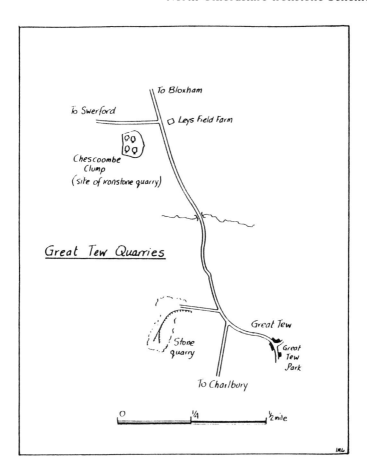

To Bloxham

To Swerford

Leys Field Farm

Chescoombe Clump
(site of ironstone quarry)

Great Tew Quarries

Stone quarry

Great Tew

Great Tew Park

To Charlbury

0   ¼   ½ mile

NORTH OXFORDSHIRE IRONSTONE SCHEME

In the 'steel boom' years of the late 1950s plans were made to develop a large area under this general heading, at first a reopening of ground incompletely worked in the past, but later extending into new territory as far as ironstone quarrying was concerned. Though none of the plans came to fruition, they deserve a mention since the legal wrangling that led to their abandonment became something of a 'cause celébré'.

The promoters, Dowsett Mineral Recovery Ltd, had as their aim the supply of ore to Richard Thomas & Baldwins Ltd, at that time building their new Spencer Works at Llanwern, near Newport, Monmouthshire, which was designed to utilize Marlstone ore from Oxfordshire, the nearest homebased source; some would be obtained from Oxfordshire Ironstone Co Ltd but it was thought that the latter would be unable to satisfy the requirements of Spencer Works when in full production.

The first proposals were relatively modest, comprising 976 acres at Bloxham and 185 acres between East Adderbury and Kings Sutton, in effect reopenings respectively of the former Bloxham & Whiston Ironstone Co Ltd quarry at Bloxham and Alfred Hickman's Sydenham Farm quarry, for working the ground they had left untouched. The ore would be transported by lorry to convenient railheads. At Bloxham no more than 40 acres would be occupied at any one time, and operations would be spread over 30-35 years; at Adderbury only 20 acres would be worked at one time, and the life of the quarry would be six to eight years. Dowsett's application for planning permission was made in April 1957 and the above figures quoted at a Public Inquiry held at Bodicote House on 16th and 17th July 1958 under the auspices of the Ministry of Housing and Local Government[1]. There was considerable local opposition even at this stage but approval of the scheme might well have been given, since the areas had already been opened up. However, it was revealed at the Inquiry that there was a possibility of further applications being made, and these were announced ten days later[2], throwing an entirely different complexion on the matter; for the area involved was this time in country hitherto unaffected by ironstone working. The 2,553 acres formed an irregularly shaped area, on each side of the A361 Banbury-Chipping Norton road between South Newington and the Swerford turn; to the north it included most of the high ground between the A361 and the road from Milcombe to Hook Norton, including Brymbo's Park Farm site, but the villages of Wigginton and Swerford were to be by-passed. South of the A361 the proposed site included Iron Down and each side of the road half way to Great Tew and including the former quarry at Chescoombe Clump.

It was estimated that the total area of around 4,000 acres now being sought by Dowsett would yield upwards of two million tons of ore per year. Haulage was to be by lorry and private concrete roads to railheads. This was a much more sensitive area, environmentally speaking, than the Bloxham-Adderbury application and aroused intense local hostility. So all the applications had to be reconsidered and in due course the Minister for Housing & Local Government ordered a second Public Inquiry[3], to be held in November 1960. By this time, Robert MacGregor & Sons Ltd had applied to reopen the erstwhile Clay Cross workings west of Bloxham, proposing to work 65 acres of the 100-acre site, of which 25 acres had already been exhausted; it was expected to yield 3,000 tons per week over 6-10 years, conveyed by dumpers over a private road to the railway. This scheme, too, went into the melting pot.

The Public Inquiry into the Dowsett applications was held in Banbury Town Hall from 8th to 18th November 1960, so that both sides had plenty of time to prepare their cases; the MacGregor hearing was held at the Town Hall 1st December 1960. It would be tedious to describe these proceedings in acrimonious detail; the interested reader will find them fully reported in the columns of the *Banbury Guardian*[4] and for a critical appraisal there is Roy Gregory's essay[5]. The basic aims of the protagonists are clear enough. Dowsett hoped to reap profit by opening up a wide area and supplying Spencer Works with the ore they needed; the opposition was determined that the ore should come from somewhere else—Wroxton or overseas, anywhere so long as somebody else had the nuisance. Of course the arguments were not set out in these terms and the matter rapidly became a political issue. On 9th May 1961 the Minister refused the applications on the grounds of potential harm to attractive countryside; and was doubtless mindful of the favourable effect his decision would have on voters.

As events turned out the whole exercise was largely a waste of time, as within a very short time there was such a sharp recession in the steel industry that Dowsetts (or Richard Thomas & Baldwins (Mineral Recovery) Ltd as they had then become) would almost certainly have abandoned their grandiose scheme. A similar scheme for the Stamford area in 1960 also came to nothing.

Footnotes

1. *Banbury Guardian*, 17th July 1958.
2. *Banbury Guardian*, 4th September 1958.
3. *Banbury Guardian*, 25th February 1960.
4. *Banbury Guardian*, 17th July and 4th September 1958. 25th February, 10th, 17th and 24th November, 1st and 8th December 1960. 11th May, 23rd November, 7th December 1961.
5. *Oxfordshire Ironstone* by Roy Gregory in *The Politics of Physical Resources*, pp.22-65. Penguin 1975.

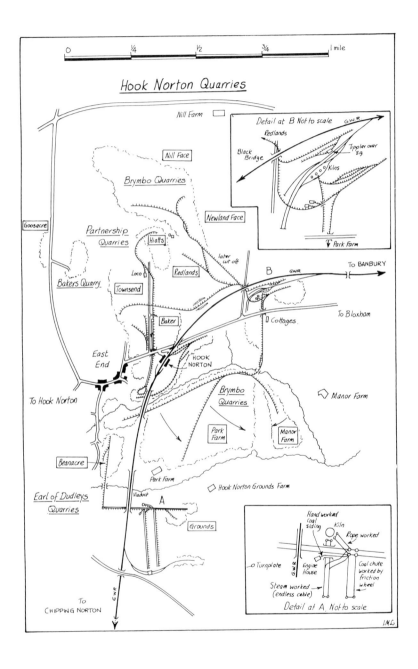

Hook Norton Quarries

HOOK NORTON QUARRIES

Owners: Hook Norton Ironstone Partnership Ltd.

The earliest efforts to establish ironstone quarries at Hook Norton were intimately bound up with those at Bloxham, as described previously, and the pattern of negotiations almost exactly similar; but whereas the developer's plans at Bloxham fizzled out and were only revived some 30 years later, the quarries at Hook Norton were established shortly after the opening of the railway. Oxfordshire Ironstone Co Ltd purchased ground on both sides of the railway site at Hook Norton station, at a date not known but probably early in 1883, as at Bloxham; this ground was conveyed to a partnership of Richard B. Looker, John Wilson and Henry Lovatt on 19th April 1884 and to the Hook Norton Ironstone Partnership Ltd on 1st April 1889. Two more small areas on the borders of the Oxfordshire Ironstone properties—on the west a piece of ground (house, cottages, orchards etc) on the edge of Hook Norton village in the possession of a family named Hiatt, and on the east side a very narrow strip—were conveyed by the Bloxham Ironstone Co Ltd to the Hook Norton Ironstone Partnership Ltd on 21st April 1888 (Oxfordshire County Archives). The first Partnership manager was Richard Looker but by 1895 he was succeeded by C. H. Looker (Kelly's Directories, 1891/5). Production seems to have begun in 1889, in which year MS records it under the ownership of 'Hutchings & Co' a long-established haulage firm of Stratford-upon-Avon, and listed in Kelly's as 'Ironstone Contractors'. There are a number of cases where the ore was extracted and/or marketed by contractors instead of by the quarry owners, and this is presumably one of them. A Manning Wardle 0-6-0 saddle tank locomotive was delivered by the makers in November 1889; she had the maker's typical features and brass nameplates *Hook Norton* on the square saddle tank; her livery is unknown but was probably the usual green, and she was housed in a shed close to the station.

The first output was almost certainly obtained from the fields immediately southeast of the station, probably by direct shovelling into railway wagons. In *The History of Hook Norton, 912-1928* (published by the *Banbury Guardian* 1928) Margaret Dickens remarks: "shortly after the opening of the railway, the first cutting of ironstone in the field was made next to the station between that and East End, by the newly-formed Hook Norton Ironstone Partnership". This is probably incorrect, operations in the 'Station Field' north of the road being started shortly after the workings southeast of the station, and the output conveyed by horse-drawn cart to the yard, tipped out and then shovelled with back-breaking energy into railway wagons. This field was probably leased from H. W. Baker, whom we shall meet again. A much larger area was acquired by purchase in the 1890s, bounded by the Banbury road (or the houses bordering it) on the south and the Sibford road on the west as far as the cross roads by the Gate Inn. This land lay west of the railway, but connection with the GWR was by necessity on the southeast side, immediately east of the station, and from a reversing point the line curved down the hillside parallel with the railway at first and then underneath the viaduct; and from a tipping dock on the north side of the line immediately west of the viaduct a 1ft. 8in. gauge tramway was laid to the quarries. The standard gauge line was steeply graded (about 1 in 30) so *Hook Norton* could have brought up only two or possibly three loaded wagons, nor could the headshunt accommodate more. The peculiarly complex layout of the narrow gauge line was too transient to appear on the OS, but the courses of former routes are shown, to supplement the reconstruction fortunately prepared for us by Alan Blencowe in discussion with an old resident of 'Hooky', Mr F. Harris; these have been confirmed by later investigations of the site in the company of Fred Beale, a former quarryman, and members of the Hook Norton Local History Group.

The narrow gauge tramway was taken under the Banbury road by a tunnel and then ran alongside the east side of a narrow lane, almost certainly on a rising gradient. The section between the road and the tipping dock, with a gradient of about 1 in 20, was operated by cable from an engine house near the far end of the lane; beyond this point the tramway was continued first on a low embankment and then in a cutting down a short slope, also cable-operated, to a bridge over a stream. The cable-worked section was probably double track for the most part, judging by visible remains. The ground slopes steeply upwards north of the stream and the tramway climbed in a semi-circular cutting to the west, then across the level ground to Hiatt's Pit (it appears that the family was associated with ground both south and north of the road).

The other main quarry was Townsend Pit, west of the green lane and with a tramway connection some 50 yards from the main road, passing under the green lane by a plank bridge. The locomotive *Florence* was transferred from Adderbury in 1892 and presumably worked Hiatt's Pit; she was housed in a small shed with a concrete floor close to the bridge over the stream. The wagons were presumably pushed over the bridge and attached to the cable one at a time, and wagons from Townsend Pit similarly attached at the junction; the full wagons would therefore use the west road, giving rise to right-hand working. The tipping dock was known locally as the 'Tip up', later corrupted to 'Kick up'. The dock was wide enough to accommodate several tubs in a row, favouring the operation of side-tipping from narrow gauge to railway, and the wooden tubs were stated to have been mainly side-tippers, with a few end-tippers. Possibly there were three or four plate-tipplers in a row, which would fit in with the title 'Tip up'; it might even be that the plates **were** kicked up!

The curious and highly uneconomic transport arrangements brought about by the difficult topography, whereby ore existing within 500 yards of the GWR was pushed around by *Florence*, hauled up one

Hook Norton Quarries (Partnership). The tunnel under the road used by the former narrow gauge tramway was repointed and blocked to serve as a pigsty; the gate on the ground to the right was used as a door. This site is now occupied by houses, and the tunnel in a private garden. Photographed April 1952. (Eric Tonks)

Hook Norton Quarries (Partnership). When the Hook Norton Ironstone Partnership went into liquidation, their standard gauge locomotive HOOK NORTON was acquired by the Great Western Railway. She was docks shunter at Weymouth and was withdrawn January 1926. This picture was taken at Weymouth shed in 1925.   (E. H. Seward)

incline, let down another, and transhipped to standard gauge in its half-mile journey, probably contributed to the financial difficulties that soon beset the company, especially as this was a time of depression in the iron industry. In 1899 the company reported (*Banbury Guardian*, 22nd June 1899) that they continued to receive large orders, but this situation did not last long; the quarries were closed at the end of May 1901 (ibid, 6th June 1901), some of the men being offered employment at the reopened Adderbury pits. The date when production ceased has not been discovered, but on 12th March 1903 an Extraordinary General Meeting passed a resolution to wind up the company. As principal creditor the GWR came into possession of the locomotive *Hook Norton*. It is told in 'Hooky' that the GWR obtained the engine by seizing it from its shed at dead of night; we hardly think that the GWR were so hard pressed as to need to resort to such melodramatic methods—but it makes a nice tale! Whether true or not, *Hook Norton* thus achieved a fame it could hardly have expected otherwise. For most of its life on the GWR, *Hook Norton* hauled boat trains at Weymouth Harbour, and was withdrawn for scrap in January 1926.

Probably soon after the departure of the locomotive, the standard gauge line was lifted and also the narrow gauge tramway as far as the engine house, but the upper portion, in the quarrying area, may have been left in position. A Mr George Allen (a solicitor) had taken over the mortgages on 1st March 1900, and acquired the land in 1904, reselling it to Brymbo Steel Co Ltd in 1909, along with the locomotive *Florence*; while the area near the main road was later worked by H. W. Baker (see appropriate sections).

Of the areas not redeveloped there are still a few interesting remains to be seen. The quarrying area near the station is revealed by the slopes of the terminal faces, and the course of the standard gauge tramway may be picked up east of the abandoned BR station site, even the sleeper marks showing in the turf; lower down the slope the trackbed passes through a shallow cutting and then through a gate and near one of the former viaduct piers. The retaining wall of the narrow gauge tipping dock was left in position and though now obscured by trees it is well preserved; it consists of a stone wall about 12ft. high and 20ft. long, with four iron stanchions of old rail protruding at 45 degrees, possibly for supporting a wooden platform or chutes over the standard gauge siding. The course of the narrow gauge incline was equally clear for many years and can be faintly discerned on the lower slopes still (1982); but about 1968 most of the higher area was covered by a housing estate. The tunnel under the main road was left intact and at some stage was pointed, part filled in and the space left was used as a pigsty, with a field gate as makeshift door. When the ground was built on, the bridge was left and can be seen at the rear of No. 11 Austin's Way; the north end is still clear and opens in Hook Norton Football Club ground on the former quarry floor. The bridge is of dressed limestone blocks with a blue brick top and blue brick courses at the top of the arch, with no traces of smoke-blackening. It is possible to see right through the tunnel, which is wide enough to accommodate two tracks.

Of the area north of the road, the evidence on the ground today agrees with the earthworks of tramway courses and quarrying activities shown on the 1922 OS, and in the text we have attempted to reconcile this with the recollections of old Hook Norton residents. Starting at the Railway Hotel and walking along the road a hundred yards westwards, we reach on the north side the 'green lane', still known to elderly residents as 'Engine Shed Lane', the starting point for exploration. The old narrow gauge tunnel (shown on the OS map as 'subway') emerges immediately on the righthand (east) side of the lane, which runs due north for 250 yards, then turns at right angles for a further 100 yards. This field on the east side of the lane has been completely excavated for ironstone, and the well-preserved face is visible for the whole length of the lane; of the erstwhile partnership tramway there is no sign, but north of the right-angle bend its course on a low embankment is clearly defined, starting at the level of the lane. Presumably the engine house was at this level but the ground between this point and the road was subsequently removed by H. W. Baker. On the west side of the lane the ground is also below original level, but in this case there is a clear indication of a tramway alongside the lane throughout its north-south length.

Mr. Flint spoke of a 'plank bridge' under the lane for the Townsend quarry tramway, but when this became unsafe the landowner removed it and filled the space beneath, so there is no sign of it now. Where the lane makes its right-angle bend the public right-of-way continues straight on, amid a tangle of tramway remains. The main partnership route is on the right (east) side, with a very shallow embankment. At a later stage, Brymbo laid an extension of their two-foot gauge system at right angles across the old partnership line to rejoin Townsend quarry, and the point where it did so is still visible, as the embankment was removed. Beyond here the downhill course of the partnership line in a deepish cutting is clearly visible and, at the foot, the bridge over the stream. A few sections of very light rail are to be seen in the bushes of the cutting.

The curving cutting of the tramway climbing the further hillside to Hiatt's Pit was very plain to see up to 1980, when Redland's Farm constructed a dam by the bridge to enclose a small reservoir for farm purposes—drowning the site of the locomotive shed—and some of the clay excavated for the reservoir was used to fill in the old tramway cutting—but its course could still (1982) be made out; ploughing has since removed nearly all traces, and better evidence is provided by the terminal 200-yard ironstone face of Hiatt's Pit; this follows the hedge line on the edge of partnership land. It starts at the outcrop (south end) and ends abruptly at the wire fence replacing the former east-west hedge. The old magazine for quarry explosives stands against the face. Beyond this point the ironstone has been removed completely as part

Hook Norton Quarries (Partnership). The face of Hiatt's Pit on 5th May 1983. The building was a magazine for explosives and was built by Brymbo.   (Eric Tonks)

of Brymbo's Redlands Quarry. The OS map shows, just round the corner of the face, an 'engine shed' that once held a stationary engine for pumping for the farm and later an air compressor used by Brymbo; a heap of stones is all that remains.

Finally, Townsend Quarry; the terminal face is a 700-yard arc, very well defined throughout and starting from the corner of Hollybush Road with the main road, and ending as the ground falls away to the stream. Between this face and the green lane there is also a short curved gullet, presumably the original tramway connection to the line alongside the green lane, west side. Further north, very faint traces of Brymbo's line across to the Townsend face can be seen. The area, though small, makes an excellent exercise in industrial archaeology, with its complex tramway and quarry layout.

When the track was taken up, a fair bit of it seems to have been sold locally for fencing, for which purpose it was cut up into convenient lengths, with small holes drilled to take wire. A number of these have been rescued by Percy Hackling and are of three types; the cable-worked portion had light rail, anchor-shaped in section with a round top, and attached to longitudinal sleepers on iron plates 6in. long by 5in. wide, with a bent-over tab for the rail. There were also some rails wihout any 'foot' for slotting into plates, but with a median rib; how these were attached to sleepers is not clear—perhaps in a longitudinal groove up to the rib or in a chair and key. Finally, some much heavier bulb-shaped rail turned up in 1984 from the vicinity of the rope-worked incline (the northern one); and some chairs — into which the rails fitted precisely, from the field where *Florence* worked—with the implication that the rail was used for the locomotive-worked section.

Hook Norton Quarries (Partnership). Members of the Hook Norton History Group explore the standard gauge trackbed, seen here on 5th May 1982, running up from the viaduct area towards the station (behind the camera).   (Eric Tonks)

Grid References

363336	Junction with GWR
364335	Standard gauge locomotive shed
360333	Standard gauge terminus
361333	Tipping dock from narrow gauge
362335	Tunnel under main road
362336	Tunnel under green lane
362340	Narrow gauge locomotive shed
362342	Terminal face of Hiatt's Pit—north end
361341	Terminal face of Townsend Pit—north end

Locomotives

Gauge; 4ft. 8½in.

HOOK NORTON	0-6-0ST	IC MW	1127	1889	13 x 18in.	3ft. 0in.	New 11/1889	(1)

(1) to Great Western Railway, 1337, 7/1904.

Gauge; 1ft. 8in.

FLORENCE	0-4-0ST	OC MW	579	1875	6 x 8in.	1ft. 8in.	(a)	(1)

(a) ex Adderbury Quarries 1892

(1) to Brymbo Steel Co Ltd, Hook Norton c.1904.

HOOK NORTON QUARRIES

Owner: H. W. Baker

Henry William Baker is described in *Kelly's Directory* as a farmer of East End, Hook Norton, and his interest in the ironstone presumably only a sideline; he was a native of Worcester and moved to Hook Norton on marrying a daughter of the Minchin family, who had held East End Farm for a century. He had two quarries, Top Pit on the road from Hook Norton to Sibford Ferris, and Bottom Pit at East End. The main quarry at the Top Pit was on the east side of the road, but there was also a very small working on the west side in the field known as Goosacre. It seems probable that the area north of the main road worked by Hook Norton Ironstone Partnership when they first started operations (Station Field) was leased from Baker and upon the failure of the company, Baker continued operations on his own account as Bottom Pit. This must have been after 1903. As *Rylands Directory* lists Baker as quarrying in 1902–06, it is virtually certain that the Top Pit was the earlier, and it is said to have had the better ore. It is believed that he started working in the 1890s. Operations were all by hand, with about 20 men and boys.

'Toppers' removed overburden; it is worth mentioning that they segregated topsoil and subsoil and replaced them in the correct order, this extra care resulting in restoration to good land and reflecting their farming background (Brymbo were not so particular, it is said, and as a result their land is still comparatively poor). The stone was hard and was prised out by pick and long levering bars, but later blasting was used. It was loaded by seven-tined forks into two-wheeled carts and taken by boys to the station yard, where it was tipped and then shovelled into wagons from a loading platform level with the wagon floor; there were about four carts serving Top Pit and three in Bottom Pit. Horses were at first kept in the fields but from 1918 in the yard and hovel at the back of East End Farm. The partnership tunnel was used for storage.

H. W. Baker died on 10th March 1915. GSM reports that the East End pit "will soon be worked out", which would presumably apply to about 1916–17. Output went to Lilleshall Ironworks, the Earl of Dudley's Round Oak Works, and to Cardiff. The date of closure is not known but is believed to have been about 1918–19. The East End quarry is a very well-defined area north of the main road, with the ironstone face alongside it, the green lane (Engine Shed Lane) and the northern edge of the field. Some of this was probably quarried by the partnership, but most of it more likely by Baker, as his excavations included the site of the partnership tramway between the road hedge and winding engine. The main Sibford Ferris road pit also displays a well-defined terminal face at the south end of the worked area, part of which is now covered by farm buildings. This pit adjoins the western partnership ground. The 'Goosacre' pit on the opposite side of the road is marked by a gullet, part of it now a pond, alongside the field side of the hedge.

Grid References

363358	East End Quarry—northwest corner
356340	Sibford Ferris road Quarry

HOOK NORTON QUARRIES

Owners: Brymbo Steel Co Ltd

Hook Norton is an out of the way place, not generally known and quite a way from Wrexham; it would be interesting to learn how the Brymbo Steel Co came to hear of the existence of iron ore there. Doubtless they were seeking such a source and, in spite of the distance, the journey by Great Western Railway throughout was fairly straightforward. They chose well; these quarries were the most successful of those at Hook Norton, lying further east than the others, with the advantage of broader areas of fairly level ground with the ore under shallow cover. The quarries lasted 50 years and were the only Midlands ironstone quarries owned by Brymbo until the latter became involved in Oxfordshire Ironstone Co Ltd—and even that did not lead to the closure of Hook Norton.

Prospecting started in 1897 and Park Farm, an area of 152 acres, was purchased from John Faulkner on 15th August 1898, together with ground to give access to the railway. The negotiations had been going on for some time, as the *Banbury Guardian* of 5th May 1898 reported that 'Brimbow' (sic) had very recently purchased Park Farm. The farm itself lay some 150 yards west of the north end of the second of the two railway viaducts south of Hook Norton station, and the principal quarrying area was the high ground, round the 500-foot contour, between the two streams crossed by the viaducts. These two streams join up a mile to the east, enclosing the workable area on that side; the railway crossed Park Farm land, some of which lay west of the railway, between it and the village. It was decided at the outset to erect calcining kilns, a set of which were in course of construction at Astrop quarries. The building of the kilns, laying railway sidings and the narrow gauge tramway to the quarries, took some time. Headquarters were set up on the south side of the GWR half a mile east of Hook Norton station, and construction of the kilns by a local contractor, E. Roberts, began in February 1899.

The kilns were of Davis Colby type, gas-fired, and thus different from the Gyers type in use at Astrop and Sydenham. They had stone bases and coned steel sides with encircling galleries, and were probably not quite as tall as the Gyers kilns; their coned sides made them resemble blast furnaces even more closely. There were two kilns originally, with

Hook Norton Quarries (Brymbo). The Packer Collection (photographs by the late Frank Packer of Chipping Norton) is a marvellous record of local scenes and events, and fortunately for us he included the quarries at Hook Norton working at the time. This one is a scene typical of ironstone quarrying before mechanisation. 'Toppers' are removing the overburden and depositing it on the worked-out ground to the right, a job with a pretty high accident rate!

(Oxfordshire Museum, Woodstock, Packer Collection)

an adjacent steam-operated lift by which loaded wagons were carried to the tops of the kilns, which were connected by a bridge with 2ft. gauge track; a rotary tippler was installed on each kiln so that ore could be transferred from the wagons. At the foot of each kiln were chutes whereby calcined ore could be discharged directly into railway wagons. Some ore was sent away raw, as required.

The quarries were served by a tramway of 2ft. gauge with 40lb. rail; as we have noted already, the narrow gauge tramways in the Banbury area were less than 3ft. gauge, differing in this respect from ironstone quarries elsewhere. The present line ran almost due south from the steam hoist, beneath the road by a brick-lined tunnel, to the Park Farm area, where it crossed the stream by an embankment and turned westwards, generally following the outcrop parallel with the stream. In

Hook Norton Quarries (Brymbo). In this 1901 view, only the first two kilns are in service. The tramway to Park Farm Quarries is at the lower level to the right, and the GWR line can be seen in the background. The kilns are of the Davis-Colby gas-fired type.

(Oxfordshire County Libraries)

Hook Norton Quarries (Brymbo). JOAN backs on to the train as the last tub is filled.

(Oxfordshire Museum, Woodstock, Packer Collection)

addition to the hoist for use with the kilns, there was a siding for direct transfer of raw stone from narrow gauge to standard gauge. There was a brick-built locomotive shed and workshops by the kilns, and immediately south of the tunnel under the road was a row of six cottages built on 11 acres of land purchased in 1898 by the company since 'labour will have to be imported, as there has been no unemployment here for a long time past'. (*Banbury Guardian*, 22nd September 1898).

The first locomotive, *Gwen*, arrived in August 1899 and was a Hudswell Clarke saddle tank of the uncommon 0-4-2 wheel formation; she had outside frames, perhaps indicating her to be basically a 3ft. gauge type with the wheels placed inside the frames to suit the narrower gauge. Another unusual feature was the footplating, all on one level on the lefthand side, but dropped by the cab on the righthand to accommodate the coal bunker, with the omission of a separate step; the cab also extended over the safety valves, to the rear of the saddle tank. *Gwen* was put to work at Park Farm quarry right away and the first consignment of raw ore was sent to Brymbo during the week ending 21st September 1899[1], and the first load of calcined ore 6th December 1899. This came from kiln 'A', and the building of kiln 'B' commenced 4th December 1899; kiln 'C' is stated in the Brymbo Magazine to have started production 25th June 1900, but local testimony says 'early in World War I', which is supported by a sudden jump in calcine production from 45,000 tons (1916/17) to 60,000 tons (1918). The fourth and last kiln came into use in June 1922.

Before 1900 the ore was almost certainly obtained from the outcrop facing the stream, but early in 1900 working west of the railway commenced, the tramway being taken underneath the viaduct; these workings were directly across the valley from the early partnership quarries. *Gwen* came to grief here on 4th December 1899—probably when the line was being extended to open up the quarry—and toppled over when rounding the curve by the viaduct pier, severely injuring her young driver.[2] *Gwen*, however, seemed to have been little the worse and carried on working the traffic unaided for sixteen years, when a similar locomotive, *Joan*, was obtained. These two locomotives had a very unusual livery (in later years, at any rate) of grey, and the brass nameplates had serif letters on a black background.

In early years of the new century operations were considerably extended; work continued—apart from a five-month closure from March to August 1901—on the west side of the railway until 1903, when the area was practically exhausted, and the Manor Farm face was opened. This was on the eastern side of the leased ground and a continuation of the outcrop, this time facing Manor Farm across the valley; working had also recommenced east of the railway on the Park Farm site in 1902. Yet another face was opened up in 1901, a small area east of the works, i.e. between railway and road, presumably by a short branch off the 2ft. line; this was part of a 40 acre site purchased in 1901.

On 2nd April 1909 Brymbo acquired a large area north of the railway. The major part comprised the ground formerly owned by Hook Norton Ironstone Partnership and which on the latter's failure had been owned by George Allen; two months later Brymbo sold two fields southeast of the station, from which the ore had already been removed, and two fields west of the Sibford road. Brymbo also acquired the locomotive *Florence*, which was immediately offered for sale[3]. The main area became known as Redlands Quarry, from the farm of that name, and four more fields were leased from H. W. Baker, between Redlands and the railway. This was primarily to give tramway access to Redlands via a girder bridge (known as 'the black bridge') under the railway at the west end of Brymbo's yard; this tramway ran over a rutted lane beneath the bridge and crossed two standard gauge sidings on the level to make a connection with the line from Park Farm by the locomotive shed. There was also a line alongside the GWR (south side) to a tipping dock and a standard gauge siding. The first working north of the railway seems to have been a small area, soon abandoned, along the north side of the railway embankment, then another face east of the partnership's Hiatt's Pit, and known as Baker's Quarry, being on ground leased from Baker; then, further north, on their own ground, as Redlands Quarry. Whitehills Farm, adjacent to Redlands, was purchased in 1916. The total area available was nearly 300 acres, and development appears to have been rapid, as GSM (c. 1917) mentions 'several working faces'. With shallow overburden, operations were by hand, and the ore was mixed in equal parts with the more siliceous ore from Park Farm; the latter area had apparently been closed for a time, probably because of increasing overburden, but the west face was reopened with a new Ruston Procter 20-ton steam navvy obtained in 1915 and working in conjunction with a large rotary screen designed to separate large stone, 'fines' and topsoil. This machine was a 'one-off' and was not very successful, as it clogged in wet weather; it was returned to Brymbo, the steam digger also, with

89

Hook Norton Quarries (Brymbo). In 1915 Ruston Proctor & Co Ltd supplied a steam digger for the ironstone, which was put through the screening device shown. The latter often clogged in wet weather, so the experiment was abandoned. Hand loading was then resumed. (Oxfordshire Museum, Woodstock, Packer Collection)

reversion to hand-working for the reduced postwar demand. An official Ruston Proctor photograph shows the 'fines' being collected in small u-section tubs. During World War I output had considerably increased (the second locomotive, *Joan*, came in 1915) and while Brymbo was still the main recipient of the output, ore was also sold to works in Staffordshire, the Black Country and South Wales. During the war there were about 100 employees and output around 5,000 tons per week, compared with the 1,000 tons of the early years.

Towards the end of the war plans were made to work ground further west, and in 1919 a line was laid parallel with the railway, along the old quarry bed, then on a very substantial embankment over a stream, across the course of the partnership tramway and beyond this to the quarry face left by partnership operations. The 1920 OS shows track this far but Mr F. Harris and other local men are positive that, though the formation was built up and ballasted, the rails were never put down and everyone agrees that Townsend Quarry was not reopened, probably because of reduced post war demand and because there was stone more easily to be had further north. 'Redlands Quarry' became the general term for the area north of the railway.

Throughout the 1920s activity at Hook Norton was at a low ebb, in common with most ironstone systems, with only Park Farm (east side) being worked most of the time, and the 'Hook Norton Notes' in the Brymbo Works Magazine contain frequent references to this state of affairs. 'Very slack, with starts and stoppages' (March 1922); and 'difficult to write of Christmas jollities and good cheer when our steel trade and particularly the iron ore part of it is suffering from a depression that is almost universal' (December 1924). Some of the men found employment building a 'new road'—probably a resurfacing—between Bloxham and Hook Norton in 1926, but several of the long-serving men left permanently in 1928–29. A far cry from the 'No unemployment here' of 30 years before! Since Brymbo was a part proprietor of Oxfordshire Ironstone Co Ltd, it is surprising that Hook Norton was not closed down in the way that Alfred Hickman

Hook Norton Quarries (Brymbo). Hand loading in Redlands Quarry, 7th September 1928. The site of this view has been identified by the disposition of the trees.

(B.G.S.)

closed Astrop and Sydenham Quarries when Hickman acquired an interest in Oxfordshire Ironstone. However, Hook Norton—for reasons unknown but which it would be interesting to learn—remained open to the benefit of local men and narrow gauge enthusiasts. The background of a 1928 photograph showing quarrying in progress enables it to be identified as Redlands, which had evidently been extended a fair distance northwards but not far west as yet.Park Farm west side was levelled to form a cricket pitch for employees about 1921.

As with quarries everywhere, there were long hours of hard manual work for meagre pay, commencing at 6.00am. Overburden was removed by 'toppers' working in pairs, one filling the wheelbarrows and the other 'running the plank' to deposit it on worked-out ground; this called for a modicum of skill in timing steps to the rhythmic bounce of the plank, which became well grooved by the iron wheels. At the quarry face the foreman allocated three or four trucks as required to each pair of fillers. The kilns worked 24 hours a day, and stone not required immediately was put on a stockpile for the night shift; and when rain stopped quarrying, the men would load stone from the stockshed. A team of nine or ten men operated the kilns, the gas for which was produced on the spot, and as it was unrefined, there was a weekly task of clearing the jets of tar. The works produced its own electricity, and "the sight of the plant lit up provided a spectacle to a village without electricity of its own at that time".[4]

In July 1926 calcining was discontinued, but the kilns were left standing and were used in the late 1930s for drying ore from Park Farm for gas-purification purposes; a man named Harmer Brown came to an arrangement with Brymbo for these tests. When the kilns were closed down, the raw ore was transferred from the narrow gauge tubs to railway wagons via a rotary tippler erected over the northern standard gauge siding, the narrow gauge being steeply graded to it; the locomotive would haul the train from the 'Black Bridge' as far as a reversing point beyond the tippler, over which the wagons were run by gravity and collected at the other reversing point for a return to the pits. The layout of the narrow gauge at the works then seemed unnecessarily intricate but was due to the piecemeal way in which it had been built up to serve Park Farm and then Redlands, and dealing with both raw and calcined stone. Stone from the two sources had to be segregated, too; Redlands was limey, requiring blasting, while Park Farm was softer, non-limey.

A third locomotive had been obtained after World War I, a Hunslet

Hook Norton Quarries (Brymbo). A closer view of the first two kilns, showing the hoist for the narrow gauge tubs.   (Collection P. Hackling)

Hook Norton Quarries (Brymbo). GWEN at work during the period of intensive operating in World War II. 22nd July 1943. The 'Black Bridge' under the GWR is obvious. Compare the photograph of the locomotive with the earlier view of JOAN, showing the other side of the engine. The picture above shows the dropped footplating under the cab.
(A. N. H. Glover)

Hook Norton Quarries (Brymbo). A rare shot of the Hunslet 4-6-0T at the foot of the bank to the tippler, 22nd July 1943. Norman Glover stands on the left.
(L. W. Perkins)

4-6-0T, *352*, similar to the one at Sydenham Quarries, and seemingly no more popular; she was painted plain black, unofficially named *Black Bess*, and in later years a stovepipe chimney replaced the original; during the 1920s and 1930s she spent most of her time in the shed, gathering dust. For use in World War II two locomotives were obtained from North Wales, both Hunslets. One was *Betty*, a standard quarry type but displaced from one of the granite quarries on Yr Eifl by diesel traction; she was painted green with red coupling rods and had brass nameplates with plain letters on a red background. The other engine was the famous 2-6-2T *Russell* of the Welsh Highland Railway, that had been abandoned in the shed at Dinas Junction since rail traffic ceased; when the railway was taken up for scrap in 1942 *Russell* was acquired through the Ministry of Supply by the Brymbo Steel Co Ltd for use at Hook Norton. She was overhauled first at Brymbo, receiving a livery of grey with black lining and red rods, in keeping with the Hudswell Clarkes; the large brass dome was polished and new nameplates were cast, the originals having been sent to York

Hook Norton Quarries (Brymbo). The famous ex-Welsh Highland Railway locomotive RUSSELL, complete with all its wheels, which was not always the case here. She is bringing in a train from Redlands Quarry, 22nd July 1943. Note the new nameplates supplied by Brymbo. (A. N. H. Glover)

Museum. The new plates had taller letters, cutaway corners and were placed higher up and further back on the tanks than the originals, and the letters had a red background.

Russell was a powerful locomotive capable of handling with ease any load made up at the quarry, but she was not designed for such work where sharp curves and uneven and lightly-laid track were only to be expected; in an effort to reduce the frequency of derailments, the leading pony truck was removed and even the rear pair of wheels at one time—but she was hardly a success at Hook Norton. To accommodate the new arrivals an additional road to the locomotive shed was provided in the form of a corrugated iron lean-to. Heavy repairs to locomotives were carried out in the workshops at Brymbo, where a length of mixed-gauge track was laid near the locomotive shed.

During the war it was normal to have four locomotives in steam—two 'big engines', *Russell* and *352*, working Redlands, a small one in Park Farm, and one shunting the yard. There were two working faces at Redlands, known as Top and Bottom Pits, operated in echelon. A 43RB dragline was obtained through the Ministry of Supply to assist production; it was employed mainly on removing overburden as at Nill Face, but was tried out as a loader for a time. According to local sources, there was also a diesel digger to remove overburden; she was evidently secondhand and has not been identified.

Hand loading remained the general rule. After loosening by a stone 'peck', the ore was forked out and the larger lumps laid aside and used to load the last tubs of the day; as the men were paid according to the number of tubs loaded, this practice enabled them to fill the last set of tubs more quickly and thus knock off a few minutes earlier. The wagons were steel, not quite straight-sided, on channel frames, with centre buffers, 4ft. 6in. long, 3ft. 5in. wide, and 2ft. 6in. high, and held about 30 cwts.[5]. Each man usually filled 20-25 tubs per day, but when dealing with the poorer Newlands Face (see below) only half that number was common. One photograph shows a V-section side tipper on the line to the tipping dock, its purpose unknown. A public footpath crossed the Redlands site and a portable wooden bridge was used to enable walkers to cross the working face.

The Redlands Quarry was gradually extended north and east over the years; the tramway passed under the 'Black Bridge', ran northwest (with an ironstone face on its northeast side) for a distance and then divided into two branches running roughly west and north. By the

Hook Norton Quarries (Brymbo). Because of wartime difficulties in obtaining film, this photograph is well below the standard of the photographer, but we include it because it shows the two locomotives obtained for use in World War II — RUSSELL in the new lean-to shed, and BETTY in the doorway of the original shed.(L. W. Perkins)

outbreak of World War II the western quarry had been exhausted, and the area further north was then developed; in 1942 the tramway route was modified to give a straighter run from the 'Black Bridge', entailing the removal of some ironstone in the process. This was the start of the Newlands Face, which proved however to be poor stone — which was probably why it had not been worked earlier, despite its nearness to the plant. A large area to the northwest was worked (still known as Redlands) and there was an east-west face on the northern edge of the workable area known as Nill Face, from the name of the farm on the hilltop above. Between them was 'Middle Face', all three forming one long arc. One night there was a landslip along a section of Nill Face, a number of tubs being buried under a large bank of clay — and they may still be there. For a short period in 1944 work stopped entirely. Quarrying at Redlands was abandoned in 1945, according to a report by T. H. Whitehead and W. J. Arkell on the Field Meeting of the Institute of Geological Sciences, 15th September 1945.

Park Farm was also worked intensively during the war, in an

anticlockwise direction, and the final face reached when work ceased in mid-1945 was almost parallel to that of Manor Farm (started in 1903), leaving a narrow strip of ground unworked between them. At the end of the war, as demand dropped off, Nill Face was the only one working, and the end was clearly not far off, for which there were a number of reasons; falling demand, the near exhaustion of stone under shallow cover, the rather outmoded transport system, and Brymbo's interest in Oxfordshire Ironstone Co Ltd, which would easily satisfy their demands; indeed it was only wartime pressure that kept Hook Norton open latterly.

The system closed in June 1946 and remained dormant for two years, presumably in case reopening should be required; but in 1948 *Russell* was removed by road to Weyhill, near Andover, an item in a sale of surplus equipment owned by the Ministry of Supply; she was purchased by B. Fayle & Co Ltd and used at their clay mines near Corfe Castle, again with many operating difficulties. The remaining plant, including 5,000 yards of 35–40lb track, four locomotives, 160 ore wagons and four kilns, was acquired by G. Cohen Sons & Co Ltd in October 1948 and dismantled in the period May-July 1949; the whole of the tramway was lifted and the locomotives remaining cut up on the spot. The wagons were sent to Tanganyika in connection with the ill-fated Groundnut Scheme.

There are quite extensive remains to be seen. The locomotive shed of brick, with slated roof and steel-framed windows with small panes and semicircular tops, is used as a workshop and timber store, while the smithy of similar construction has been converted to a dwelling house. In front of the locomotive shed are the concrete supports for rails where they passed over the quarry line from Park Farm, evidently only just clearing the tubs. The kilns were about 20ft. in diameter, of ironstone blocks with lime mortar in the two oldest kilns and cement in the last two; the bases of the older pair were demolished to provide stone for use on the house 'Kilnstone' in the village, and the other two were demolished early in 1983. The course of the BR line and its siding into the works are very well defined, and between them stands the bank on the top of which ran the narrow gauge en route to the tippler, with the concrete wall at the end, but part of this bank was excavated in March 1983 in the course of demolishing the last two kilns. To the east of this area, alongside the main road, can be seen the isolated quarry with a presumed connection to the main system at its northwest corner. The yard was, by 1983, occupied by Taylor Engineering Ltd,

Hook Norton Quarries (Brymbo). A photograph taken after closure, showing the complete set of kilns.
(Collection Eric Tonks)

who describe their premises as 'Brymbo Works, Hook Norton', thus nicely retaining a link with the past. South of the road the six cottages are still occupied and the nearby narrow gauge tunnel under the road was intact in 1961; but a few years later the cutting on the north side was filled up. The south portal is still open however and the construction shows blocks of stone for walls, and rough stone over the three courses of blue brick forming the tunnel roof; stones on edge line the parapet. The tunnel was in 1984 used for 'Discos'! The adjoining field, across the tramway from the cottages, shows signs of having been quarried close to the line, probably from very early days, as there is no clear record of when it was done.

The course of the tramway towards Park Farm can be made out, including the high embankment over the stream, and some rail in the hedge growing across the route. The Manor Farm terminal face is well defined and nearly paralleled to the west by the terminal gullet of the Park Farm workings; in 1983 a start had been made in filling the gullet so that cultivation could be taken right up to the face. Across the middle of the site runs a hedge with several trees in it, suggesting possibly that it is the original, never disturbed for some reason; but the land is level with the hedge on each side, so the latter was possibly replanted with trees, which is uncommon but not unknown (e.g. Colsterworth)—or the trees might be spontaneous, as in the terminal gullet itself. Some finds of Roman material were made from time to time but in general were not reported in case it caused a holdup in production; they were just reburied! At the bank top alongside the stream there are faint traces of the tramway to the Park Farm quarry west of the railway, and even better traces beneath the viaduct site, even the sleeper marks being apparent; beyond these the course of the line can faintly be made out, but there is no distinction between the Brymbo workings and those of the Earl of Dudley's Beanacre Quarry.

At the Redlands site the courses of the tramways could still be made out some ten years after closure, with the newer line on ash ballast standing some six inches higher than the older route, on earth; all these traces have now disappeared but the main quarrying areas are still pretty plain, and we will take them clockwise, which is very roughly the order in which they were developed. Close to the railway is the earliest face, well defined, and if we walk along it we reach the fine embankment laid down to reach and reopen Townsend Quarry on former partnership ground; beyond the embankment the line is laid more or less on ground level and can be traced across the partnership's main tramway en route. Of the original 'Bakers Quarry' there is practically no trace, but some pieces of rail have been used in the hedge here. Next north is the first Redlands Quarry proper, cutting off the top of Hiatt's Pit (also partnership). North of here is a wide expanse of rather rough ground, with a low wooden fence on the west side, replacing a hedge, while to the east can be seen the smoothed-over Newland's Face—some of the smoothing done by a 'crawler' and some by Nature! More obviously ironstone is the terminal gullet of Nill Face along the northern edge of the quarried area, with Nill Farm perched on the hilltop; further west, the limit of quarrying is marked by a general lowering of ground levels and the transition from hedge to fence. The cattle and sheep on the site eye us warily—but our thoughts are of days long past when neat little grey engines quietly chugged along with their rakes of steel tubs.

Finally, in Banbury museum we can see a possibly unique collection of quarrymen's tools presented by George Dumbleton—a hammer, a stone fork, stone peck and a shovel. As with the partnership, rail survives as fence posts, and Percy Hackling has specimens revealing a

100

variety of cross sections. The older rails seem to have been fishplated.

Footnotes

1. From Brymbo Works Magazine, under 'Events of local interest'. Various issues in the period 1920-30, in Clwyd Record Office. My thanks to Philip Hindley for bringing these to my notice.
2. *Banbury Guardian*, 7th December 1899.
3. *Contract Journal*, 14th April 1909.
4. Roger Gorton, *The Hook Norton Ironstone Companies*; Cake & Cock Horse, Autumn 1982. p 17.
5. Richard Thomas & Baldwins Ltd, Irthlingborough files in BSC Archives. *Inspection of calcining kilns*. Report 10th September 1915. M.Barrett.

Grid References

369339	Kilns
369340	Tippler from narrow gauge
368339	Locomotive shed
369338	Tunnel under main road; and cottages
368335	Bridge over stream
369333	Manor Farm face—north end
368334	Park Farm face—north end
371339	Quarry east of works—terminal face
368339	Black Bridge
365338	Embankment—east end
361339	Crossing of partnership tramway
363342	Redlands Quarry—west end
364344	Newlands Face—north end
363345	Nill Face—east end

Locomotives

Gauge; 2ft. 0in.

GWEN	0-4-2ST	OC HC	523 1899	8 x 12in.	2ft. 0in.	New 8/1899	Scr.6/1949
JOAN	0-4-2ST	OC HC	1173 1915	8 x 12in.	2ft. 0in.	New 10/1915	Scr.6/1949
352	4-6-0T	OC HE	1264 1917	9½ x 12in.	2ft. 0in.	(a)	Scr.6/1949
RUSSELL	2-6-2T	OC HE	901 1906	10¾ x 15in.	2ft. 4in.	(b)	(1)
BETTY	0-4-0ST	OC HE	1101 1912	7½ x 10in.	1ft. 8¼in.	(c)	Scr.7/1949

(a) ex Ministry of Munitions 5/1919.
(b) ex Welsh Highland Railway, per Ministry of Supply, 5/1942; overhauled at Brymbo Works before being sent to Hook Norton.
(c) ex Penmaenmawr & Welsh Granite Co Ltd, Yr Eifl Quarries, Trevor, Caernarvonshire, per Thos. W. Ward Ltd, 9/1942.

(1) to B. Fayle & Co Ltd, Corfe Castle, Dorset, via Ministry of Supply, 1948.

Gauge; 1ft. 8in.

FLORENCE	0-4-0ST	OC MW	579 1875	6 x 8in.	1ft. 8in.	(a)	(1)

(a) ex Hook Norton Ironstone Partnership Ltd c.1904.

(1) Offered for sale 4/1909. To Dick, Kerr & Co Ltd, contractors.

Quarry Machines

No. 20 S. Navvy		RP	434 1915			New 6/1915	(1)
D. Shovel			?			(a)	s/s
43RB D. Dragline		RB	6708 1942	1Cu.Yd.	75ft.	New 3/1942	(2)

(a) ex ?, c.1941

(1) to Brymbo Ironworks c.1920.
(2) to Stanton Ironworks Co Ltd, Woolsthorpe Quarries, Leicestershire, 10/1946, per MOS.

HOOK NORTON QUARRIES

Owner: The Earl of Dudley

This quarry system was separated from the others lying to the east of the village by a narrow but deep valley (carved by a tributary of the river Swere), and the main workings lying in the shadow of the railway viaduct that crossed it were served by a siding leaving the GWR immediately south of the viaduct, which was the second one beyond Hook Norton station. The ore was an outcrop site, a counterpart to the Park Farm Quarry worked by Brymbo on the broad spur north of the valley; but in this case the outcrop was a comparatively narrow strip that ran practically east-west from the vicinity of Hook Norton Grounds Farm to Sands Lane south of Hook Norton. From the start the ore was calcined in a coal-fired kiln in the valley bottom; this worked on a batch process, ie. filled, burnt and then emptied, while those at Brymbo operated on a continuous system.

Hook Norton Quarries (Earl of Dudley). A group of quarrymen, with the tools of their trade at The Grounds Quarry.   Collection P. Hackling)

103

Hook Norton Quarries (Earl of Dudley). Surprisingly, several photographs of the calcining kilns have survived, mostly with parts obscured by steam and smoke. The main tramway line can be seen in front of the kiln, and the ramp by which tubs were hauled up to fill the kiln. The Grounds Quarry lies to the right and Beanacre Quarry to the left, both just off the picture. The wagons were hauled by a cable, powered from the engine house in the centre of the picture. The kiln was operated by a batch process.

(Oxfordshire County Libraries)

The tramway system was unique. In the first place, all operations were in the valley bottom, and output had to be conveyed by a cable-worked incline **up** to the railway—contrary to the common practice of ore being lowered from hillside outcrops to railways in the valleys; there was no other instance in the Midlands ironstone industry, though there was such a system in the Brendon Hills in Somerset. Secondly, because the areas to be quarried initially lay in a long narrow strip, advantage was taken to connect them by a straight cable-worked tramway, ideally suited to such conditions. Third, the full tubs were hauled up a concrete ramp to the top of the kiln, which was equivalent to the system at Astrop, where the tubs were taken along a viaduct to the kilns on lower ground; Sydenham and Brymbo used cages to haul up the tubs. We are fortunate in having a map and description provided by Alan Blencowe from information supplied by Mr F. Harris.

A double track ran along the valley floor from The Grounds quarry at the east end to the other quarry (probably known as Archill from the field name) at the other. This track was carried over the incline to the GWR siding by a concrete causeway and then under the GWR viaduct. Full tubs used one track, empties the other. From a couple of turnplates sidings led to the kiln, where the full tubs discharged their loads from the top of the ramp; after calcining, the ore was tipped into tubs at the foot of the double incline and hauled by cable to a gantry over the standard gauge siding at the summit, emptied and returned to the kiln. Tubs could be exchanged between the 'main line' and incline by means of connecting sidings. There was also a further double incline, used only for bringing coal for the kiln down from the standard gauge, so that in this case steam haulage was not required, a friction wheel sufficing in the usual way; a single siding ran from the foot of the incline (where it met the 'main line') to the engine house, where two vertical boilers supplied a two-cylinder engine. There were also short branches to the working faces, worked by horse or possibly by hand. When the Archill Quarry was exhausted, the tramway was extended northwards to the corresponding level north of the stream; this was Beanacre Quarry, taking the field name, and the cable was presumably taken round a pulley to make the required angle. The wagons were turned on a metal plate, temporarily unclipped from the cable the while. The stream was negotiated by a dip in the line, carried on metal sheets at little above ground level. Beanacre (Benicker by pronunciation) Quarry adjoined the south end of Brymbo's Park Farm West Quarry. The tubs were of iron and the output went to the Earl of Dudley's Round Oak Works.

The Earl of Dudley purchased land for quarrying in the summer of 1898[1] but there were some difficulties in commencing work on the site[2]; the date of opening is believed to have been in 1901, in which year the kiln was under construction[3], and in the weekly report of W. J. Hudson (Manager of Easton-on-the-Hill quarries) to the Marquess of Exeter is a comment that "Lord Dudley is working his own Oxfordshire Mines"[4]. Operations were however very erratic, with several temporary closures, and working finally ceased in April 1916, the plant being dismantled in 1920. The 1922 OS map shows that the tramways had all been lifted, but the concrete causeway, ramp and kiln were still existing, and presumably dismantled at a later date.

As might be expected, the remains are not impressive, but a few points of interest are to be seen. If we plod up Sands Lane and cross over the abandoned BR cutting, there is a patch of rough ground to the north side by the bend in the lane, and between that and the BR bridge a hollow on the presumed site of the winding drum; this hollow was in 1978 being filled in with earth and rubbish, and the trees and bushes on the site grubbed up in July 1982 to permit cultivation. A concrete block at the top of the 'coal road' remains.

Of the incline down the hillside there is very little to be seen, but it is worth going down to have a look in the valley bottom. The site of the 'works'—all steam and smoke in its heyday—was marked by an area of rough ground where the kiln and engine house stood, but this too was bulldozed for cultivation in August 1982; however, the pond was left for drainage purposes, and a shallow tramway cutting lies almost beneath the site of the railway viaduct, the ground here being too hard for turning over. The site of the heap of calcined ore by the side of the kiln is denoted by the dark red colour of the soil, which is otherwise light brown; and there is an ash patch near the boilerhouse site. In a little spinney one can find strands of discarded cable; most of the cable had been acquired by some local men in the hope of selling it, but it lay rusting in a barn at the top of the hill for years, until removed by Friswell. To the west a lightly hollowed area denotes the Archill Quarry; north of the stream can be seen the remains of the slight embankment (called 'The Jetty') leading to Beanacre Quarry, identified by rough ground and the terminal face at the back of the houses along Ashburton Lane and Rope Way (the latter refers to rope-making, not to the tramway!). In late 1982 preparations were under way for building houses on the quarry site. To the east of the central area is the well-defined terminal gullet of The Grounds Quarry, on the south side of the worked-out area; the latter stretches to the outskirts of Hook Norton Grounds Farm and in a line three fields to the east, denoted by the slope of the land. These observations were made in 1982 by the author in the company of a group of Hook Norton Historical Society members. Percy Hackling, one of these, has specimens of rail—fairly heavy too and of two profiles; the sleepers were most unusual in being of a cross shape, according to the recollections of a former worker.

Footnotes.

1. *Banbury Guardian*, 14th July 1898.
2. *Banbury Guardian*, 12th January 1899.
3. *Banbury Guardian*, 28th August 1901.
4. *W. J. Hudson's Report*, 24th December 1902.

Grid References

364323	Transfer to GWR/Winding drum
361327	Kiln
364326	The Grounds Quarry—east end
359331	Beanacre Quarry—north end
361327	Tramway relic

NORTHERN GROUP

The Northamptonshire Quarries

Byfield and Charwelton are an odd pair of outlying quarries, both in Northamptonshire but of the Marlstone Rock formation so prominent a feature of North Oxfordshire. Both were products of World War I and eventually came under Staveley control, but with many vicissitudes in their history, with intermittent working. The railway connections were out of the ordinary too—Byfield on the SMJ and Charwelton on the GCR main line. Their setting in very attractive countryside, and their isolation, make them of peculiar interest.

BYFIELD QUARRIES

Owners: Northamptonshire Ironstone Co: Northamptonshire Ironstone Co Ltd from March 1922: Byfield Ironstone Co Ltd from 24th November 1928.

The Byfield quarries were the most successful of the few ironstone quarries connected to the Stratford-on-Avon & Midland Junction Railway, and in later years provided the most important originating traffic east of the GWR line, such that the closure of the two were inevitably linked. In earlier years, however, the fortunes of the quarries under changing economic conditions exhibited as many ups and downs as the original tramway route! Ownership was not continuous, but in three quite distinct phases, with different policies and operating ideas.

The first owner was J. W. Pain, Byfield being the first of the three quarries opened up by him when he severed connection with James Pain Ltd, the others being Bloxham and Whiston. The nominal operator at Byfield was Northamptonshire Ironstone Co. (as at Bloxham) and production commenced in May 1915, according to GSM, the earliest workings being immediately adjacent to the SMJR about half a mile west of Byfield station, and served by a standard gauge tramway making a west-facing junction. This line was then extended

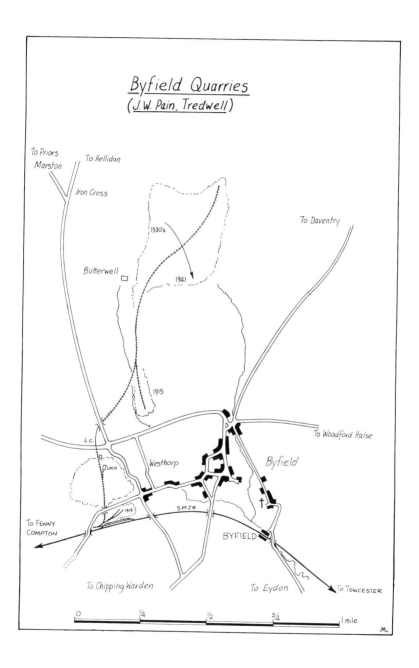

almost due north, taken beneath a bridleway by means of a brick arch and ending at a locomotive shed a quarter mile from the SMJR juncton; working continued on the east as far as the village of Westhorp (which adjoins Byfield) and also to the west, where GSM records working in August 1917. This was part of a 22-acre site leased from Miss M. J. F. Farebrother for 21 years from 25th March 1915, with two fields north of the railway and one field south; a much larger area, 117 acres, was leased from Miss Farebrother for 21 years from 25th March 1916, this lying north of the Byfield-Boddington road, between the footpath to Iron Cross and the stream to the east. The *Banbury Guardian* of 15th July 1917 also reported that there were plans for a 1,000-acre extension east of the road from Byfield to Priors Hardwick; this is partly confirmed by a lease for 30 years from 25th March 1917 for 420 acres with A. R. T. Cartwright; there is no map attached to this lease but surely it must refer to the same area, possibly Ironhill Farm.

The SMJR Minutes of 13th June 1918 record the despatch of 60 wagons per day in 1918, when the sidings were to be extended, with help from the Ministry of Munitions. Surprisingly, details of a type of wagon used at Byfield have survived, a 20-ton seven-plank hopper built by Watts, Hardy & Co Ltd of North Shields for the MOM, painted grey and lettered in white shaded with black 'Empty to Northants Ironstone Co, Byfield'. A No. 12 Ruston Proctor steam navvy was used during this period; the *Banbury Guardian* of 19th July 1917 states that there were 'two American diggers' but we can ignore the 'American' as a common term for a mechanical excavator; but there was evidently a second machine here.

Official information during Pain's ownership is lacking, but the postwar recession brought about periods of idleness, as in most quarries; in 1922 a limited company was formed with J. W. Pain as sole director, but the economic situation did not improve, and the quarries were closed down at an unknown date, probably early in 1925; in May 1925 a Receiver was appointed and efforts made to sell the quarries as a going concern as reported in the *Kettering Leader* of 1st May 1925. By this time the tramway had been extended along the west side of the locomotive shed, crossing the Byfield-Wormleighton and Westhorp-Iron Cross roads on the level, to the larger area leased in 1916 from Miss Farebrother, north of Byfield village, starting at the southwest corner; like the earlier workings, these were under shallow cover. On the tramway earthworks were reduced to a minimum, resulting in some frightful gradients—1 in 33 up to and beyond the shed, followed by a downward stretch of 1 in 25 beyond the level crossing and another 1 in 33 up to the workings. Drivers had no option but to rush the banks with loaded or empty wagons and, as the track was only flat-bottomed and not too well-laid, the engines suffered accordingly.

The first locomotive, *James*, was a four-coupled Peckett saddle tank of 1904 from the Glendon quarries of James Pain Sr, but all later locomotives were six-wheelers; *James* cannot have been of much use on the banks and was probably confined to the quarry near the SMJR. Two more Pecketts, both 0-6-0ST but even older than *James*, were obtained, but neither lasted long, *Northfield* being sent to Bloxham in 1918 and *Jeannie Waddell* cut up five years or so later. Another locomotive at this period was a Hudswell Clarke named *Lance B. Pain* after James Pain Jr's brother, who assisted him at Byfield and elsewhere. *James* was painted in Peckett's standard livery of green, lined black edged yellow, and possibly the others also.

The locomotive shed was a single-road building of black painted corrugated iron with a rounded roof and three iron 'pots'. At some time a 10ft. extension narrower than the main body was added at the front.

Byfield Quarries. Locomotive shed, about 1939, with original line to quarries beyond. HC 347 in the doorway. Note the rosebay willowherb on the right, already well established here. (Collection Eric Tonks)

Byfield Quarries. Much of the quarry work was in the hands of vintage steam locomotives such as MW 1235 photographed here in the quarry 9th October 1950. She shows little evidence of having been rebuilt by Pecketts!

(Ken Cooper/IRS Collection)

The quarries were acquired by a local farming family named Tredwell under the style of Byfield Ironstone Co Ltd, a most unusual arrangment for the time, 1928, when nearly all the quarries were under the control of the iron and steel companies; in 1928 in fact James Pain Ltd, the largest independent ironstone operator, was taken over by Stanton Ironworks Co Ltd. A fresh lease was drawn up between Miss Farebrother and Jeffery Tredwell for the same areas as the 1915–16 leases, for 21 years from 29th September 1928. The Westhorp quarry north of the railway had already been largely exhausted, the area south of the railway untouched except for a small quarry, shown on the OS, that was probably exploratory only. Working continued north of Byfield and the tramway was extended to enter the quarrying area close to a group of farm buildings called Butterwell. As with J. W. Pain, little information has survived concerning this phase of activity, which was purely a local one. Few changes were instituted by the Tredwells and working again seems to have been intermittent, depending on the market; presumably the owners had their farming interest to rely on, and quarrying to some extent a sideline. A steam dragline was acquired; the date is uncertain but probably it came during the Tredwell era.

A further locomotive was acquired, a Manning Wardle 0-6-0ST; she actually came from Peckett's, who had obtained her from a customer in part exchange for a new locomotive. She had been overhauled and painted in standard Peckett colours of green, lined black edged yellow, with red coupling rods, and she proved a worthy purchase, lasting almost to the end at Byfield. Like the Hudswell Clarke, she was of a type favoured by contractors and the two engines had many characteristics in common, though by different makers. The Hudswell Clarke was renamed *Byfield* by the new owners and had a livery of light brown lined black, edged yellow and the name painted in yellow on the tank.

Towards the end of the 1930s demand increased and four members of the Tredwell family leased 422 acres to the company; this comprised Manor Farm and Dodds Farm, between the Farebrother lease and the Byfield-Charwelton road, and the term was 30 years. Some time earlier a further 35 acres had been leased or purchased from J. H. Hiatt. The company was however not best equipped to meet wartime demand; the quarry machines were old and so were the locomotives, and these factors—possibly coupled with a somewhat casual approach to production requirements—led to radical reorganisation in 1941 through the auspices of the Ministry of Supply Iron & Steel Control; it was arranged for the Ironstone Department of Staveley Coal & Iron Co Ltd (who were then managing Charwelton quarries) to take over Byfield quarries[1]. No time was lost in implementing this decision, the Farebrother lease being assigned to the reorganised Byfield Ironstone Co Ltd 4th July 1941, and the Tredwell lease 5th July 1941. Four Ruston Bucyrus diesel quarry machines (three of them new) were obtained—two 43RB draglines, a 55RB dragline, and 43RB shovel; and a new six-coupled saddle tank of the type supplied by Bagnalls to Staveley quarries at this period. This was named *Byfield No. 2* and had the standard livery of mid-green lined black edged yellow on the inside and red on the outside, green wheels and nameplates of cast brass, with letters on a red background. *James*, which had been out of use for some time, was cut up.

There were great improvements in the tramway also; the worst of the banks were removed by altering the course of the line to a longer but easier route further west, the original line being cut short by the first level crossing, thus relegating the locomotive shed, stores etc, to a spur. These changes were authorised by an agreement with the county council 5th July 1941. The new line to the quarries was also modified, with cuttings and embankments in place of the gradients, and a tunnel beneath the Iron Cross road put in instead of the level crossing. There was still however a level crossing, protected by a flagman,over the Wormleighton road.

Under Staveley management quarrying commenced south of the area worked by the Tredwells; an initial gullet was driven eastwards from Butterwell in June 1941, and working southwards clockwise thence up to 1953. The course of the upper end of the tramway was then altered from northwards to eastwards across the southern part of the recently worked-out ground, over the streams by concrete bridges, then north to open up ground on the east side, which was worked in south to north strips in the period 1953-58.

A wayleave for this new layout was the subject of an agreement with M. J. F. Farebrother, for 25 years from 1st January 1952. Some chaired track with ex-BR chairs, was used from the bridge under the Iron Cross road towards the pits, but mostly it was still flat-bottomed track. The distance from working face to the BR junction was about two miles. From 1958 ground to the north, towards Iron Cross, was worked clockwise until the closure; for this last phase, where heavier overburden was encountered, a 5W diesel-electric walking dragline was purchased to replace the 55RB.

Obviously, working was more intensive from 1942, and two locomotives were in daily use, one in the pit (usually one of the old locomotives) and one working to the main line railway, usually the Bagnall, the two exchanging loads at a loop near the entrance to the quarrying area. The routine differed little from day to day, and interest centred more on changes in locomotive stock and quarry machinery, the former in particular offering quite a variety of interest. Under the special emergency measures preceding the Invasion of Europe in June 1944, Byfield and Charwelton quarries were closed and the men transferred to other work, usually at Oxfordshire Ironstone Co Ltd. The locomotives were greased up and stood in their sheds, but shortly afterwards *Byfield No. 2*, which was still MOS property, was sent to Oxfordshire Ironstone. One of the 43RB draglines was commandeered for opencast coal production but was returned in the following year, when production was resumed, with the help of *Cherwell*, sent later in the year from Charwelton, when these latter quarries were closed again. She was sister locomotive to *Byfield No. 2*.

Byfield Quarries. A Ruston Bucyrus 43RB shovel loading wagons, May 1949. Note how shallow is the overburden, a feature common to most marlstone quarries.

(B.G.S.)

Byfield Quarries. For some time a stable companion with, and near contemporary to, MW 1235 was SIR BERKELEY, seen here outside the shed on 4th November 1961. The rather crude cab was added at Cranford Quarries. (Ivo Peters)

Locomotive MW1235 was repainted in the new standard Staveley livery of light green with red rods (1955); and HC 347 was in the same livery when returned, nameless, from Charwelton in 1956. By 1958 the HC had virtually ceased work, and when *Cherwell* required a retubing and other attentions, another Manning Wardle, *Sir Berkeley*, even older than 1235, was obtained from Cranford, so that in the summer of 1959 it was possible to enjoy the sight of two vintage Mannings at work together. *Cherwell* was back in service again by September 1959 and MW1235 was withdrawn in the following month. In the second week of May 1960 a large Avonside arrived from Staveley Works, *No. 3 Avonside*; she had a maroon livery, but in August was given a coat of shiny black paint, with red rods and backing to the plates. While this was being done *Cherwell* worked the traffic unaided, and *Sir Berkeley* does not seem to have worked again; *No. 3* resumed her duties in September 1960. There were then four to six trips of eight 27-ton tipplers daily. The two relics, MW 1235 and HC 347, were shunted

Byfield Quarries. AVONSIDE No. 3 taking water while standing on the original line to the quarry, 8th September 1960. The locomotive shed is on the left and the new line to the quarries diverges from beyond the shed, near the bridge in the background.

(G. H. Starmer)

about the premises, standing either at the end of the old line beyond the engine shed, close to the road, or down at the BR sidings in the old quarry; details of these intricate movements have been described elsewhere[2].

Protracted repairs to the roof of the locomotive shed were commenced in 1962, when the rear portion with one 'pot' was reroofed to a triangular section, with a new truss. The front portion, with two 'pots' was removed, but work on replacing it, using—it is believed—smoke chutes from Sproxton shed, was halted by the closure of the quarries. During this time, two of the engines were open to the sky.

In the light of the sorry history of ironstone quarrying in the late 1950s and 1960s, the closure of Byfield could hardly cause surprise, but in this case it does seem that the decision was a sudden one. Working was then in the area between Iron Cross and the stream running down to Byfield, and from 1962 there were two faces almost at right angles;

Byfield Quarries. Looking towards the former SMJ line from the junction of the lines to quarries (right) and locomotive shed (left), 8th September 1960. The office is beyond the bridge, on the right. This bridge has now completely disappeared, and is filled in to road level.

(G. H. Starmer)

one running southeast to northwest, and a smaller one parallel to the Iron Cross-Hellidon road, both working clockwise. At the time of shutdown, a half-completed gullet in the direction of Iron Cross suggested the intention to work right up to the road. Quarrying at the southeast-northwest face ceased on 26th January 1965, while the very last load was taken from the Iron Cross face 12th February 1965 and despatched to Renishaw Ironworks the same day.

Fourteen men were retained for six months on dismantling and restoration, which commenced immediately, *No. 3 Avonside* being used on the task of track-lifting; and as the former SMJR line was already closed, BR sent a special from Woodford to pick up wagons loaded with rail. By the end of April the only track remaining was from the BR line to the locomotive shed and the loading bay by the stores beyond, and two months later this had been reduced to a short length of track by the locomotive shed and loading bay to accommodate the two remaining locomotives. The older engines had all gone; about March 1962 MW 1235 had been hauled up to the quarry near Iron Cross and dismantled by using the dragline; part of its saddle tank was used as a cattle trough for a time. *Sir Berkeley* went to the Keighley & Worth Valley Railway Preservation Society 19th January 1965, following negotiations with Roger Crombleholme. The HC was last noted by the author 21st January 1965, with snow piled high on the saddle tank and drifted behind the chimney after a snowstorm the previous day; she disappeared very shortly afterwards. The Avonside went to Cranford quarries for further work, but *Cherwell* remained until taken by road on 11th August 1966 for display at New Street Recreation Ground, Daventry. She was given to them at the request of the Surveyor's Department of the Borough Council[3].

Restoration of the site to agriculture had been going on rapidly; on the west side of the bridge under the Iron Cross road there was a heap of earth excavated from the cutting, and this was used to level the site. The parapets of the bridge consisted of six concrete uprights with four horizontal steel tubes between each pair; for some years these parapets remained as a reminder of the bridge, though corn was growing on the filled-in cutting in 1966. The bridge under the bridleway to Westhorp, near the locomotive shed, was filled beneath with earth. Early in 1967 the locomotive shed was sold to a local farmer and was dismantled, and the weighhouse was also demolished about the same time. A 'Trains cross here' notice where a footpath crossed the line at Westhorp was purchased by an enthusiast. In spite of these continuing changes, some evidence of the quarries and tramway can be seen by the assiduous searcher, the most clearly defined near the SMJR route, i.e. the oldest part. The first quarry, right by the SMJR, is still to be seen in its abandoned state. The bridleway bridge has been filled in, as already noted, and north of this, quarried ground is to be seen on each side of the faintly visible quarry tramway trackbed; that on the east has along its northern edge an ironstone 'bench', while to the west the quarried area is crossed by an obvious replacement hedge of hawthorn and elder, but near the bridleway the ground has not been quarried and the hedge is the original, with other species such as maple growing. North of the quarried area the course of the **old** tramway route is clearly defined; the site of the locomotive shed is denoted by a scooped-out space, and just beyond lie the old stores and a wooden shed alongside the trackbed. The site of the level crossing of the Byfield-Wormleighton road can be identified—far more

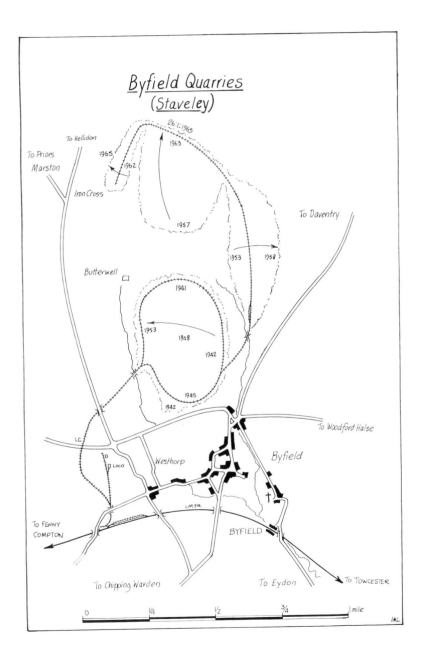

Byfield Quarries
(Staveley)

To Hellidon

To Priors
Marston

26·1·1965

1965
1962
1963

Iron Cross

1957

To Daventry

1953 1958

Butterwell

1941

1953

1948

1942

1945

1942

To Woodford Halse

LC

D Loco

Westhorp

Byfield

LMSR

To Fenny
Compton

BYFIELD

To Chipping Warden

To Eydon

To Towcester

0   ¼   ½   ¾   1 mile

easily than the newer crossing to the west, which is indicated by a wire fence on the south and a gate on the north side. There is no sign of the course of the line.

As we walk up the road to Iron Cross, we need sharp eyes to pick out any traces; a length of wooden fence on the east side might be the site of the one-time level crossing, but of the bridge that carried the road over the later route a little more can be seen; the parapets have gone but there is a replacement hedge of hawthorn and elder on each side of the road, contrasting with the rest of the hedge, that contains mature trees. The main quarrying area between this road and the Byfield-Charwelton road has been returned to agriculture of course, but if we take the footpath from Byfield to Iron Cross, we come first to a sunken area of ground on the right (east) side where quarrying took place in the 1940s; of the earlier workings to the west almost nothing can be seen, probably because they were outcrop. Continuing north, replacement hedges are obvious and continue east of Iron Cross, and a wire fence west of Butterwell. The 'old quarry' shown on the 1945 OS has disappeared completely, but the hedge on its west side is interesting as being a replacement one for the northern three quarters and original for the southern quarter. The crossings of the two streams can be identified; the stream running down to Westhorp is culverted and has a concrete cover for twenty yards, with a hawthorn hedge on the top now; and there is a concrete culvert over the stream to Byfield. This is a very pleasant walk in any case, and seeking these reminders of the past gives it an added attraction.

Footnotes

1. Letter 16th March 1966 from Sir Frederick Scopes. In 1941 he was Director of Home Ore, and the recommendations followed his visit.
2. *Industrial Railway Record*, Vol 2, p 317. 'Byfield & Charwelton'.
3. *Northampton Chronicle & Echo*, 27th July 1966.

The Northamptonshire Quarries

Grid References

509528	Junction with SMJR
509529	Bridge under bridleway
509531	Locomotive shed
509532	Stores
509533	Old level crossing with Wormleighton road
508533	Later level crossing with Wormleighton road
509535	Bridge under Iron Cross road
511542	Butterwell
518537	Bridge over stream
510548	Final face near Iron Cross — south end

Locomotives

Gauge; 4ft. 8½in.

Name	Type		Builder	No.	Year	Cylinders	Wheels	Ref	Notes
JAMES	0-4-0ST	OC P		996	1904	10 x 14in.	2ft. 6½in.	(a)	Scr.c.1941
NORTHFIELD	0-6-0ST	OC P		717	1898	14 x 20in.	3ft. 7in.	(b)	(1)
JEANNIE WADDELL	0-6-0ST	IC P	Reb.AE	464	1888 1898	16 x 22in.	4ft. 0in.	(c)	Scr.c.1923
BYFIELD (LANCE B. PAIN to c.1928)									
	0-6-0ST	IC HC		347	1892	13 x 20in.	3ft. 3in.	(d)	(2)
-	0-6-0ST	IC MW		1235	1893	12 x 17in.	3ft. 0in.	(e)	Scr.1963
BYFIELD No.2	0-6-0ST	OC WB		2655	1942	15 x 22in.	3ft. 4½in. New 2/1942		(3)
CHERWELL	0-6-0ST	OC WB		2654	1942	15 x 22in.	3ft. 4½in.	(f)	(4)
SIR BERKELEY	0-6-0ST	IC MW	Reb MW	1210 1909	1891	12 x 18in.	3ft. 0in.	(g)	(5)
No.3 AVONSIDE	0-6-0ST	OC AE		1919	1924	15 x 20in.	3ft. 6in.	(h)	(6)

(a) ex James Pain Ltd, Glendon East Quarries c.1915.
(b) ex Griffiths & Son, Skelmersdale Colliery, Lancashire.
(c) ex Great Mountain Colliery Co Ltd, Carmarthenshire c.1917.
(d) ex Furness Shipbuilding Co Ltd, Haverton Hill, Co. Durham c.1920.
(e) ex Peckett & Sons Ltd c.1929; prev. Westleigh Lime & Stone Co Ltd, Burlescombe, Somerset.
(f) ex Charwelton Quarries c.10/1945.
(g) ex Cranford Quarries 5/1959.
(h) ex Staveley Ironworks 4/1960.

(1) to Bloxham Quarries 1918.
(2) to Charwelton Quarries c.2/1951; ex Charwelton 12/1956. Scr 2/1965.
(3) to Oxfordshire Ironstone Co Ltd 9/1944.
(4) to Charwelton Quarries 12/1947; ex Charwelton 1/1948. To Daventry Brough Council, New St. Recreation Ground, 8/1966.
(5) to Keighley & Worth Valley Railway Preservation Society, Haworth, 1/1965.
(6) to Cranford Quarries 9/1965.

Quarry Machines

No.	Type	Maker	No.	Year	Capacity	Reach	Date	Notes
No. 12	S. Shovel. Rail	RP	268	c.1908	2½ Cu.Yds.	27ft. 6in.	(a)	s/s
No. 10	S. Dragline	RH	747	1923	1 Cu.Yd.	49ft. 6in.	(b)	(1)
43RB	D. Shovel	RB					(c)	s/s
43RB	D. Dragline	RB	5899	1941			New 7/1941	(2)
55RB	D. Dragline	RB	5900	1941	2 Cu.Yds.	70ft.	New 12/1941	(3)
43RB	D. Shovel	RB	5705	1941	1¾ Cu.Yds	22ft.	(d)	(4)
5W	DE. Walking Dragline	RB	21925	1957	4½ Cu.Yds.	135ft.	New 5/1957	(5)

(a) ex ?, c.1915 (New to E. C. Edgar).
(b) ex ? (New to Bradford Corporation Sewage Dept.).
(c) ex ?
(d) ex Ministry of Supply, Blaenavon, Monmouthshire (prev. Charwelton Quarries). Purchased from MOS 1946.

(1) to Elliotts Sand & Gravel Ltd, Brighouse, 12/1946.
(2) to MOS for coal production 1944; ex MOS 1945. To Midland Ironstone Co Ltd, Scunthorpe.
(3) to Sproxton Quarries 9/1965.
(4) to Desborough Quarries 1964.
(5) to Richard Thomas & Baldwins Ltd, Wansford Quarries, 1965.

CHARWELTON QUARRIES

Owners: Park Gate Iron Co Ltd; Park Gate Iron & Steel Co Ltd from 14th June 1919.

Byfield and Charwelton quarries have always been thought of jointly, and the enthusiast would almost invariably call at both when in the area even if he were on foot—they were that close, yet isolated by some ten miles from any other ironstone quarry. Both were very much in the country, they were comparable in size, and their history spanned almost the same period. Even the Ministry of Supply in World War II lumped them together; when Bloxham quarries were closed down on MOS instructions, Clay Cross complained bitterly [1] that their working quarry should be so treated when 'old and abandoned mines such as Charwelton and Byfield' were expensively equipped for reopening. They were however not alike in details, even in environment; Charwelton is a limestone area with a characteristically richer flora than the predominantly clay pastures of Byfield, and was generally the more attractive scenically. Historically, on the other hand, Byfield was more interesting; as we have seen, the first half of its life was in the hands of two separate independent operators, itself a rarity, before coming into the Staveley fold. Charwelton was always in the same ownership, resulting in the survival of records covering its whole operating history.

Charwelton quarries were only a mile or two from Byfield quarries by crow flight, but the bulk of Charwelton Hill (now with the TV relay station on the top) lay between them, hence Charwelton's unique (amongst ironstone quarries) connection to the Great Central Railway's main line to Marylebone. The standard gauge tramway made an end-on junction with a spur from Charwelton goods yard, the actual point of junction being marked by a gate across the track and a change from chaired to flat-bottomed track and from stone to earth ballast; the entrance to the goods yard was protected by a GCR signal. The tramway then took a west-north-west course, climbing for about half a mile, with two gated level crossings to farms; for most of its route to the quarries the line paralleled the Charwelton-Priors Marston road, though separated from it by a hedge. About three quarters of a mile from the junction were situated the offices, locomotive shed—a modern iron-framed structure of brick and corrugated asbestos sheeting with windows high in the walls—workshops of corrugated

Charwelton Quarries. The BR junction as it was—Charwelton Station with a B1 4-6-0 on a train. Line from quarries comes in at right through the gate. September 1955.

(G. H. Starmer)

Charwelton Quarries. As it is now—Charwelton station site. The gate from the trackbed to the quarries is in the same place. Beyond can be seen traces of the old platforms but the yard is heavily overgrown. 19th October 1985. (A. Cocklin)

iron and a weighhouse, and here the line turned away from the road slightly to run west-north-west to the north of Cherwell Farm to reach the quarrying area beyond. The tramway was constructed by Price & Sons.

Three leases for ironstone were obtained at the beginning; Cherwell Farm in Charwelton parish (224 acres) from the executors of Mrs Johns of Staverton, and an area of 146½ acres north of the Charwelton-Priors Hardwick road and in Hellidon parish from Vivian de Courcy Hughes, were both for 40 years from 29th September 1916, while parts of Clem Vengeance Farm (176½ acres) in the parishes of Charwelton and Byfield from Mrs Caroline Harrod and others was for 39½ years from 25th March 1917, ie. all three to end concurrently. A fourth lease for 41 acres from 25th March 1919 was negotiated with Wm. Harris Potter; this was south of the Warwickshire border, west of the lane to Iron Cross, and was never developed. A uniform royalty of 3d per ton was agreed for all four properties.

Fortunately the surveyor's maps showing the areas quarried each half year have survived, and we can see how the various areas were successively opened up. About a third of a mile beyond Cherwell Farm the tramway reached a farm track and it was here that production commenced about May 1917, the date quoted by GSM. The first workings (up to 1920) were east of the farm track, then west from 1920 to 1927, with breaks in production in 1922 and 1926. The track runs to the farm quoted in the lease and shown on the contemporary OS map with the sonorous title of Clem Vengeance—what a splendid locomotive name it would have made!—but by the 1945 OS the farm title had been changed to the relatively insipid Bromtrees. More extensive quarrying then took place between Cherwell Farm and the above-mentioned farm track, working anti-clockwise in the years 1921/23-28. There seems to have been a further break in production in 1929, but the tramway was evidently extended over the worked-out area west of Cherwell Farm to develop quarries west and northwest of Clem Vengeance. Working was clockwise from near the latter towards the Hellidon-Iron Cross road, but ceased again in June 1933. The tramway was left in position, with one man responsible for maintenance, until December 1939, when the system lay dormant until May 1941, in which month the Ministry of Supply stepped in. An agreement, confirmed in a letter of 19th August 1941, was made by which the Ministry of Supply were to provide additional equipment to enable Charwelton to produce 3,000 tons per week, Park Gate being regarded as a contractor to the Ministry.

Up to then, operations had been fairly small-scale, in line with the times, and there was a minimum of mechanical equipment—though this was obtained new. In the quarries there were two steam machines, both 'specials'—an 8-ton 'combined loading and baring excavator' and a 20-ton rail shovel described as a 'combined excavator and grab'; this latter was fitted with a 35-foot extension and grab attachment, and in 1920 was transferred to the Midland Ironstone Co Ltd at Scunthorpe. On the tramway was a Manning Wardle six-coupled saddle tank, appropriately named *Charwelton* and painted a warm red-brown lined black edged with yellow, with brass nameplates; she was the sole locomotive, as far as is known, for several years, and probably thoughout the slack times of the 1920s. At some uncertain date she was assisted by a very ancient Manning Wardle named *Holmes*, from Park Gate works; this information comes from Industrial Locomotive Society records. After Charwelton had closed down in 1933, *Holmes* was sent to Pitsford quarries, where she bore the No. 2, the name presumably being painted out.

When the quarries were reopened on a wartime footing in 1941 there were many improvements in the interests of increased production, as

Charwelton Quarries. Manning Wardle locomotive CHARWELTON, the original engine that handled the traffic unaided up to World War II. She is now on the Kent & East Sussex Railway.(Leicester Museums, Art Galleries and Records Service (Newton Collection))

Charwelton Quarries. The unusual Yorkshire Engine locomotive, *No. 8*, being flagged over the level crossing from Hellidon quarry in September 1955. (G. H. Starmer).

at Byfield. Three new Ruston-Bucyrus diesel quarry machines were supplied—a 55RB dragline, a 37RB dragline and a 43RB combined shovel and dragline, continuing the tradition of the steam machines. On the tramway two brand-new locomotives arrived in February 1942; *Cherwell*, one of the familiar Bagnalls with a livery of green lined black edged red on the inside and yellow on the outside, and red-backed brass nameplates; and *Hellidon*, a 'pre-Austerity' Hunslet with a livery of black lined red and also with cast brass nameplates (others of this class on ironstone work had transferred names only). Cherwell is the name of the river that flows towards Banbury and Hellidon is a nearby village. All these machines came through the Ministry of Supply. Management of the quarries was placed in the hands of the Ironstone Department of Staveley Coal & Iron Co Ltd, coming under the supervision of the latter company's Area Manager.

The Clem Vengeance quarries were reopened in 1941 and in the following year a new face (Brown's Pit) was opened a quarter mile to the north, in the angle of the crossroads; but the stone here proved to be poor in quality and working ceased in 1943. *Hellidon* went to Oxfordshire

Charwelton Quarries. HC 347 during its spell on loan from Byfield. Photographed about 1953, outside the shed, with the usual line of roadside trees as background.

(J. G. 'Bill' Brown/courtesy B. D. Stoyel)

Ironstone Co Ltd, and the 43RB later sent away for opencast coal production. The Clem Vengeance (or Bromtrees as it was now called) face was also closed in 1945, and the lease determined in 1948, with the last locomotive being sent to Byfield; the reason for the closure was probably reduced demand. A branch from a reversing junction to an entirely new quarrying area, north of the Charwelton-Priors Marston road, had been put in, but got no further than the level crossing; but the crossing was left in to preserve the right-of-way in view of the growing reluctance of County Councils to allow level crossings; the present one owed its existence to wartime priority.

Once again the Charwelton quarries fell silent except for the four weeks 18th December 1947 to 15th January 1948 when *Cherwell* returned to remove wagons stored on the line, but were reopened in May 1951 with fresh mechanical equipment—brand new in the case of quarry machines (a shovel and a dragline) but decidedly old fashioned on the locomotive side. The 'new' locomotives comprised our old friend HC 347 from Byfield and a neat little Yorkshire Engine 0-4-0ST

Charwelton Quarries. *No. 5,* cut-down Bagnall from Park Gate steelworks, near the loco shed.

(K. Cooper/IRS Collection)

from Park Gate ironworks. The latter was an uncommon design, with square saddle tank, painted black lined with yellow and with a brass 8 on the front of the chimney; and though only a four-wheeler, she was in excellent fettle and was the main performer in the quarries thenceforward. The Hudswell Clarke, on the other hand, was in poor condition generally; in 1955 she was painted in the then standard Staveley livery of light green with red rods, losing the name *Byfield* in the process, but at the beginning of 1957 was replaced by another locomotive, *No. 5*, from Park Gate ironworks. This was another curiosity, a little Bagnall with cut-down chimney and dome and cab placed low on the frames; she too was painted black with yellow lining and numbers. It is interesting to note that the first five locomotives at Charwelton were by five makers.

Rails to the last workings at Bromtrees were lifted and the branch to the quarry north of the Priors Marston road was completed, this time with some chaired track, and a water supply was installed at the level crossing. This new quarry, in Hellidon parish, was by far the largest on the Charwelton system and was worked anti-clockwise in a sweeping arc as far as the Hellidon road from the crossroads. In the centre of the quarried area was Attlefield Barn, which was not touched. Rail operations were comparatively simple, with both locomotives in steam normally; one (usually *No. 8*) working between pit and reversing junction, and the other engine—HC 347 or *No. 5*—between the junction and BR. A flagman was maintained at the level crossing. The usual load consisted of eight 16- or 17-ton tipplers, but on one occasion a double load was being taken to the crossing and got out of hand; the crew 'abandoned ship' en route but fortunately there was no traffic on the road and serious injury was averted.

Thus Charwelton continued to operate in its pleasant unspectacular way, and as the main quarry was approaching exhaustion fresh areas were opened up; a small area south of the level crossing and a long narrow strip between the tramway and road west of the shed and workshops; both of these were worked in 1959–60; according to Len Pridmore these were owned by 'Spencer' and presumably required a fresh lease. Because of diminishing traffic one locomotive sufficed, each being used three weeks at a time in turn; and *No. 28* (Andrew Barclay 1987 of 1930) at Park Gate Steelworks, which had been earmarked for Charwelton, did not arrive. The last quarry was in a new area south of Cherwell Farm and a branch tramway was put in from a junction a third of a mile beyond the locomotive shed, and running east-south-east through a belt of trees. This line was constructed in 1961 and the line to the Hellidon quarry lifted from the loop on the main tramway near the junction to the new pit, except for that in the level crossing. In September a small amount of stone was brought out up the steep slope from the new quarry, but was apparently not of the quality hoped for. The Charwelton system was closed 18th November 1961 'for an unknown duration' as being uneconomic at the current level of demand; in this district all along Charwelton seems to have been the one to be closed rather than Byfield. The shed buildings were however repainted in light green. The system remained in this moribund condition for eighteen months, and many enthusiasts called to see the locomotives; to do this it was necessary to place a ladder against the shed wall, from which one could peer through the high windows at the saddle tanks liberally coated with bird-droppings. The track to the new quarry was left in position, possibly in the hope that better stone might be obtained on reopening; and there was still some good ore across the road, that could be fetched out by lorry if necessary.

There was no reopening however and in June 1963 track lifting commenced; by October the locomotives stood in the ruins of their dismantled shed on the only bit of track beyond the gate to the BR goods yard, where the sidings were removed in 1964. The locomotives were cut up on the spot, just too soon for preservation efforts to be successful, and the dragline was used to level the tramway route, but the lineside fences were left in position and indeed were still so in 1969 for most of the way to the office area and beyond to the reversing spur to Hellidon quarry. In this year a group of bungalows was built on the site of the yard beyond the office.

As at Byfield, traces of the system have to be sought, for the scars on this pleasant rural landscape have healed well. At the BR station site the gate that once protected access to the tramway is still at its original angle, not in line with the fence, but of the tramway nothing can be seen as it parallels and then recedes from the road; but as it returns to the roadside, part of the original lineside fence can be noted. The office and locomotive shed area is the most obvious point of interest; the yard is occupied by bungalows but the concrete base of the demolished locomotive shed remains, used for storing equipment. The former workshops and shed, both of green-painted corrugated iron and in good condition, are apparently used for farming purposes. There is little to be seen beyond here; the roadside pits have disappeared and so has the last (1961) pit that was quite deep but never properly developed—it appears to be completely

Charwelton Quarries. Locomotive shed, showing the last two locomotives, *Nos. 8* and *5* (nearer the shed). July 1961. (G. P. Roberts)

Charwelton Quarries. The level crossing site, looking towards Hellidon Quarry. This track has now gone. (S. A. Leloux)

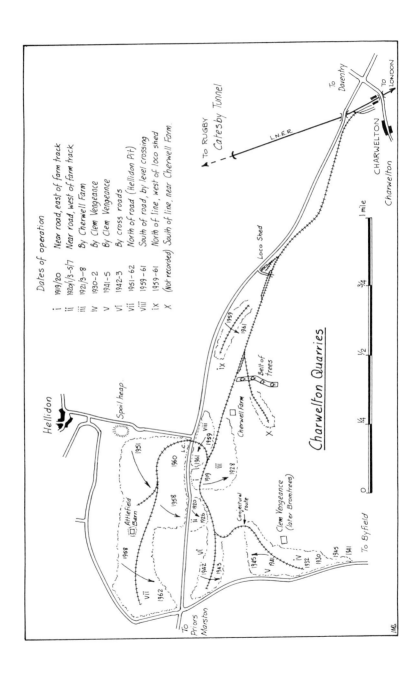

Charwelton Quarries

Dates of operation

i   1919/20   Near road, east of farm track
ii   1920/1/3-5/7 Near road, west of farm track
iii 1921/3-8   By Cherwell Farm
iv   1930-2   By Clem Vengeance
v   1941-5   By Clem Vengeance
vi   1942-3   By cross roads
vii 1951-62   North of road (Hellidon Pit)
viii 1959-61   South of road, by level crossing
ix   1959-61   North of line, west of loco shed
x   (not recorded) South of line, near Cherwell Farm.

levelled. There is no sign of the level crossing of the track to Cherwell Farm, nor to that to Bromtrees, though the track shows a drop where quarrying has occurred. Of the road level crossing to the Hellidon quarry, a slight difference in the texture of the road surface is all that can be seen, as the gates have been replaced by hawthorn hedges. Some of the original wire fences bounding the tramway remain, however. Beyond the level crossing site the fields on each side of the road are at the lower level as left after ore extraction, and replacement hawthorn hedges are very obvious; note the hedge between Attlefield Barn (in the middle of the Hellidon quarry site) and the road—this is a full original hedge for a hundred yards or so, then a hawthorn replacement. We then turn left at the crossroads towards Iron Cross and note signs of quarrying near the crossroads and then in the neighbourhood of Bromtrees—the old Clem Vengeance pits. The sunken ground extends to a quarter mile south of the farm, and on the opposite side of the road is clear evidence of further quarrying, and along the roadside is a row of white posts to prevent accidents. However, this must have been a much earlier quarry, presumably for building stone, and has no connection with the Charwelton workings we have been discussing. Finally, it is worth mentioning the fine views to be had along this section of road overlooking the valley.

Footnotes

1. Letter 1st January 1942 to the Director of Home Ore, MOS.

Grid References

535563	Junction with LNER siding.
526568	Locomotive shed.
517572	Level crossing with Priors Marston road.
511576	Attlefield Barn.

Locomotives

Gauge; 4ft. 8½in.

CHARWELTON	0-6-0ST	IC MW	1955	1917	15 x 22in.	3ft. 9in.	New 12/1917	(1)	
HOLMES	0-4-0ST	OC MW	345	1871	12 x 18in.	3ft. 0in.	(a)	(2)	
HELLIDON	0-6-0ST	IC HE	2415	1941	18 x 26in.	4ft. 0½in.	New 2/1942	(3)	
CHERWELL	0-6-0ST	OC WB	2654	1942	15 x 22in.	3ft. 4½in.	New 2/1942	(4)	
(BYFIELD)	0-6-0ST	IC HC	347	1892	13 x 20in.	3ft. 3in.	(b)	(5)	
No. 8	0-4-0ST	OC YE	784	1905	14 x 20in.	3ft. 3in.	(c)	Scrll/1963	
No. 5	0-4-0ST	OC WB	2659	1942	12 x 18in.	2ft. 9in.	(d)	Scrl2/1963	

(a) ex Park Gate Ironworks c.1930.
(b) ex Byfield Quarries c.2/1951.
(c) ex Park Gate Ironworks 2/1952.
(d) ex Park Gate Ironworks 1/1957.

(1) to Sproxton Quarries 3/1942.
(2) to Pitsford Quarries c. 1935.
(3) to Oxfordshire Ironstone Co Ltd 1/1943.
(4) to Byfield Quarries c. 10/1945; ex Byfield 12/1947. To Byfield 1/1948.
(5) to Byfield Quarries 12/1956.

Quarry machines

No. 8	S. Shovel/Dragline	RP	496	1917	1½ Cu.Yds.	25ft.	New 8/1917(a)	(1)	
No. 20	S. Shovel. Rail	RH	501	1918	35 Cu.Ft.	26ft. 6in.	New 2/1918(b)	(2)	
55RB	D. Dragline	RB	5704	1941			New 4/1941	(3)	
43RB	D. Dragline	RB	5705	1941			New 5/1941	(4)	
37RB	D. Dragline	RB	6564	1941	1½ Cu.Yds.	45ft.	New 10/1941	(5)	
43RB	D. Shovel	RB	12508	1950	1¾ Cu.Yds.	22ft.	New 10/1950(c)	(6)	
54RB	D. Dragline	RB	12509	1951	2 Cu.Yds.	70ft.	New 1951	(6)	

(a) Combined loading and baring shovel.
(b) Combined shovel and grab, with 35ft. extension.
(c) Built without front end equipment; fitted as shovel with that originally supplied with 5705 (supplied as shovel and dragline).

(1) to Lamport Quarries c.1934
(2) to Midland Ironstone Co Ltd, Scunthorpe 1920.
(3) to Midland Ironstone Co Ltd, Scunthorpe.
(4) to Ministry of Supply, Blaenavon opencast coal site 1944. Later to Byfield Quarries, 1946.
(5) to Eastwell Quarries.
(6) to Sproxton Quarries c.3/1962.

The Oxfordshire Quarries

Ironstone has been quarried in the Edge Hill district for centuries for building purposes, and the famous Hornton quarries supplied stone for local churches and buildings further afield, while the 'ironstone villages' are as much a part of the local landscape as their limestone counterparts of the Cotswolds; the stone is still being quarried for decorative purposes. Edge Hill is a steep tree-clad slope overlooking the Vale of the Red Horse (so called from the likeness once cut on the hillside but long since ploughed up and now afforested); from this escarpment the land to the east slopes more gently but is much dissected by streams feeding the Cherwell. The area is scenically very attractive but sparsely inhabited.

The use of the stone as a source of iron was a late development because of the lack of convenient transport; the only railway was the GWR main line up to 1873, when the SMJ entered the district—but the only ironstone traffic accruing from that was via aerial ropeway from the Burton Hills, an outlier of Edge Hill. It is perhaps surprising that there was no attempt to build a branch from the GWR to tap the vast reserves west of Banbury; the terrain was somewhat difficult but no more so than the Eaton area, penetrated by the GNR in the 1880s; or Loddington, served by the MR branch in 1891. Anyway, nothing of this kind seems to have been mooted and even when the overriding demands of World War I required the problem to be tackled it was by other means, and it is these railway developments that have lent so much interest to the area, with the ill-fated Edge Hill Light Railway on the one hand and the very busy Oxfordshire Ironstone Co's system on the other.

WROXTON QUARRIES

Owners: Oxfordshire Ironstone Co Ltd.

We have used the heading 'Wroxton Quarries' to indicate to the reader, particularly the younger reader, the centre of activities; but to the contemporary enthusiast they were always referred to as 'Oxfordshire Ironstone Quarries', which all understood. It was the largest ironstone system after Corby, but it was purely an ironstone operation having no direct associations with an iron or steel works; it may therefore justifiably be regarded as the zenith of ironstone quarrying in this country, worthy of study in its own right. Fortunately its history has been very fully preserved; because of its size and its relatively easy access, it has been a favourite spot for enthusiasts—industrial railway enthusiasts in particular—to whom the management was always sympathetic. As a result we have many reports, observations and photographs from the amateurs; and when the much regretted (and a couple of years before quite unexpected) closure came, the Works Manager entrusted the whole of the company records to archives. There is thus no shortage of material to draw upon and it is impossible to include it all in any history; the chronicler has to decide what of the minute recorded details may safely be condensed, while indicating the scope of the information to anyone who might wish to develop in greater depth any particular aspect. The ironstone quarry student will nowhere find more compactly available records.

Formation, Equipment and Early History

The formation of the company has been interestingly described by Sir Frederick Scopes in his *The Development of Corby Works*'; usually we know only of the results of boardroom discussions, rarely of the preliminaries and the element of chance that often plays a vital part. Colonel W. C. Wright, a director of Baldwins Ltd, had been seconded to the Ministry of Munitions under Sir John Hunter, director in charge of Home Ore Production; thus it came about that Baldwins Ltd took steps to implement the desire of the MOM to increase substantially the production of iron ore in the Midlands. Proposals to develop the Edge Hill area were already under consideration, and Alex Mackay, Baldwin's mining engineer, was asked to meet George Bond, who was

138

acting for the Earl of Dudley, one of the parties concerned in the Edge Hill scheme. Mr Mackay evidently realised the shortcomings of the latter, notably the rope-worked incline involved, and suggested a joint effort to open up an area nearer Banbury, with a connection to the GWR; Mr Bond declined, and Mr Mackay proceeded on his own—but not for long, for early in the negotiations for leases he met an old friend, J. S. Hollings of Brymbo Steel Co Ltd, presumably engaged on a similar mission. As a result the two companies acted jointly in the lease applications; this was in May 1917.

It was decided to develop a large area, the quarter compass from north to east of Wroxton, which was comparatively level and with the ironstone but a few feet below the surface. This ground was in the ownership of Trinity College and Christ Church College, both of Oxford, and Lord North of Wroxton Abbey, from all three of which leases were granted to Baldwins and Brymbo jointly from 1st January 1917. The official titles of the lessors are quaintly interesting in themselves; 'The President, Fellows and Scholars of the College of the Holy and Undivided Trinity, Oxford': 'The Dean and Chapter of the Cathedral Church of Christ, Oxford': and 'William Henry John Lord North Baron North'. The acreages involved were respectively 1,205, 340 and 722, the first two completely in the parish of Wroxton-cum-Balscott, the last one spilling over into Neithrop and Drayton, but 55 acres of the Drayton section were surrendered in 1925. The term was for 60 years and the royalty a uniform 3½d per ton of 2,400lbs. A lease for ground at Hanwell on the same terms (60 years from 1st January 1917) was granted by Earl de la Warr. Finally, ground further west, in the parish of Shenington, was leased from Clark Middleton in 1918 and purchased as from December 1929.

Some of the historical relationships are not irrelevant; Sir Thomas Pope, a favourite of Henry VIII, purchased Wroxton Abbey in 1537, following the dissolution of the monastery, and in 1554 bestowed the estate on Trinity College, of which he was the founder, while retaining the right of his family to remain as tenants. The last of the Pope family to occupy Wroxton Abbey died unmarried and his sister married Francis North (later Baron Guilford); thus the North family came into possession, lasting from 1681 to 1932, when the leases were surrendered to Trinity College (Victoria County History of Oxfordshire Vol. IX, p.176).

Returning to 1917; the joint interest of Baldwins and Brymbo was crystallised in the formation of the Oxfordshire Ironstone Co Ltd,

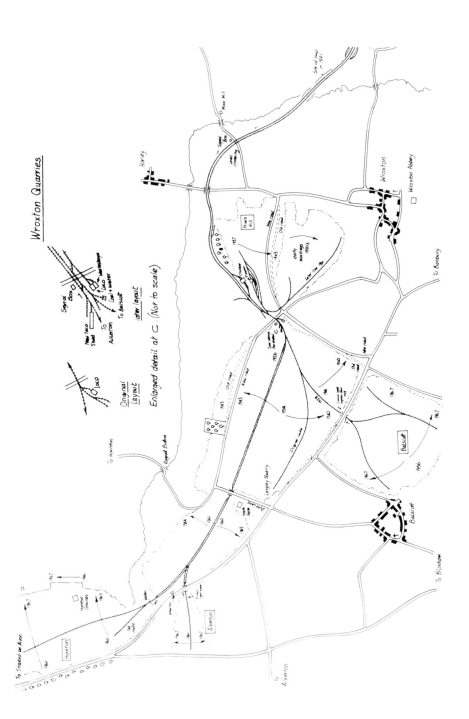

Wroxton Quarries

Wroxton Quarries

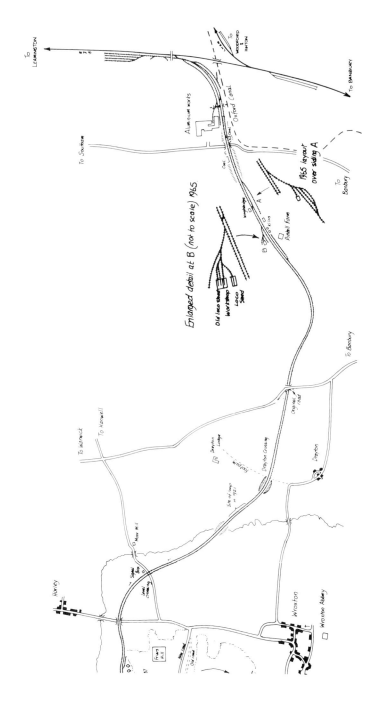

Enlarged detail at B (not to scale) 1965

1965 layout over siding A

registered 29th June 1917 with a capital of £10,000 apportioned between Baldwins and Brymbo in the ratio 3:2. In the following year, however, Baldwins acquired a controlling interest in Brymbo, so the whole of Oxfordshire Ironstone capital was in their control before production began. This was some way ahead; for while the ore was near the surface, getting it to the railway was not an easy matter. Wroxton is 500ft. above sea level, the GWR line 300ft. and the ground between the two picturesquely broken up into a series of valleys, ruling out any line on the 3½ mile crowflight distance. Three routes were put forward for consideration of the Ministry of Munitions, who had agreed to foot the bill for the construction of the railway (the term 'tramway' is hardly applicable here) and to help if necessary in acquiring the land. The route adopted was the middle one, the others being to the north via Earl de la Warr's Hanwell estate, and to the south through the Balscott estate of Sir Anthony Cope; the latter gentleman expressed his annoyance by putting up for auction Balscott Manor Farm, which included ironstone-bearing ground that Baldwins and Brymbo had hoped to lease. There was not much difference in the distances of the three routes, that selected following the courses of a number of streams in order to maintain reasonable gradients, mostly with the load, in its five miles to Wroxton; the original route included two crossings of the canal, which the MOM suggested be avoided, as was done.

No time was lost; representatives of the MOM visited Banbury 5th May 1917 and within two weeks had appointed Topham, Jones & Railton Ltd to build the railway, which would be taken over by O.I. at postwar values as at two years after the declaration of peace. The provision of rolling stock was not included in the cost of the railway, but, as will be seen, Government help was apparent in obtaining locomotives and plant. The contractors applied for the allocation of 250 German prisoners-of-war to work on the project; accommodation for these was found in the former workhouse and adjacent buildings (except for the hospital), 'the tenants having been removed from them'; not luxurious by any means but better than the tents originally proposed! The railway, sidings and plant necessitated a number of further leases, wayleaves and purchases of land, which we do not propose to list but can mention a few points of special interest.

At the GWR end there were to be four sidings, each 1,200ft. long, with accommodation for 60 wagons. The line had to cross the important Banbury- Southam road and the original application to have a level crossing was replaced by an authority from Banbury

Corporation dated 31st December 1917 to build a bridge with 16-foot headroom, girder-based on concrete abutments and brick walls. Finally, the main locomotive shed and workshops were on ground purchased from Banbury Cooperative Industrial Society Ltd 13th July 1920; this was part of Pinhill Farm and it should be noted that this is the spelling on all official documents, though sometimes appearing (as on the OS maps) as Penhill Farm.

The main line connection was put in 7th August 1917 and construction began in 1917 and proceeded through 1918. The contractors assembled a formidable array of equipment, practically the whole of it from work elsewhere; included were five Manning Wardle locomotives, four Wilson steam navvies, nearly 100 wagons (mostly 'Ship Canal' type tippers) and eighteen 2-foot gauge 'Jubilee' wagons. Most of these arrived between August 1917 and January 1918. In this connection there is an interesting note in the records of the Oxford Canal, extracted by Mr H. J. Crompton, to whom I am indebted: 'Below Bridge 160—Oxfordshire Ironstone Co's crane road—September 1917', from which it may be inferred that some of the constructional materials arrived by water.

Production commenced in January 1919, according to an extract from *Iron & Coal Trades Review* dated 10th January 1919, kindly provided by Gordon Green. This states: 'One Bucyrus and one Marion American diggers are being erected for the quarry operations, and consignments of ore have already been despatched ... on withdrawal of the German prisoners, local labour will be employed to a large extent'. O.I. hired two locomotives and two navvies from the contractors on 1st April 1919 to help bring the total to the estimated initial requirement of three of each. The ore was despatched in the raw state, but plans for calcining were soon introduced; a board minute of 7th August 1919 authorised the construction of experimental kilns, while in the meantime practising open calcining in heaps.

Ouput in 1919 was small by later standards—81346 tons—the heavy wartime demand being already over, and it dropped to a mere 112 tons in 1922; but there was no question of closing down. On the contrary, consolidation and expansion were the keynotes, so that the company was in a commanding position, well equipped to meet demand when it rose again. There was even some expansion in the available quarrying area, following negotiations with Alfred Hickman Ltd. The latter company, as we know, owned quarries south of Banbury at Astrop and Sydenham Farm, both fairly small and the former nearly exhausted; Hickmans therefore acquired ground north of Banbury in the vicinity of Balscott, Shutford and Epwell, in the form of 195 acres purchased from Sir Anthony Cope in December 1918, plus further ground leased from Lord Saye & Sele. Hickmans did not attempt to develop these properties immediately, there being no necessity while their other quarries were functioning, but the completion of the O.I. railway system afforded such convenient access that they approached Baldwins at the end of 1920 to see if mutually satisfactory arrangements could be made. Hickmans were by then in the control of Stewarts & Lloyds Ltd, and Mr S. J. Lloyd visited Banbury in February 1921 to assess the position, reporting favourably on Baldwin's proposal to join forces in O.I. As a result, 50 per cent of O.I. shares were purchased in the name of Alfred Hickman Ltd 24th August 1922 and the Board was reconstructed; instead of three Baldwins and two Brymbo directors, there were three each from Baldwins and Hickmans. The first Board consisted of Col. John Roper Wright, Col. William Charles Wright, John Cecil Davies (Baldwins), Sir Henry Beyer Robertson, James Spencer Hollings (Brymbo); the new Board consisted of Sir John Cecil Davies, J. S. Hollings, Alex Mackay, Wm. Hutchinson, S. J. Lloyd, H. A. Lennox Leigh.

History, 1923-1956

The Hickman properties were transferred to O.I. 5th March 1923; the Baldwin and Brymbo leases had been assigned to the company on 24th June 1920. Those parts of the Hickman properties in the parishes of Shutford and Epwell were sold in 1925 to G. C. Bond, who represented the Edge Hill Light Railway, which was planned to tap these areas—though in fact it never did. The merger with Hickmans brought about the demise of the latter's small quarries within a few years, probably sooner than if Hickmans had acted independently. It is somewhat surprising that Brymbo's Hook Norton quarries did not suffer the same fate; the Board discussed this point at meetings on 7th July and 6th August 1920, and it was agreed to place the management of the Hook Norton quarries under Alex Mackay, who had been appointed General Manager of O. I. on 3rd August 1917—but, as we have seen, Hook Norton carried on until the end of World War II.

There were no further major changes in company structure; external changes in the steel industry resulting in the Hickman–Baldwins participation being changed to Stewarts & Lloyds–Guest Keen &

Nettlefolds had little direct effect on the affairs of O.I., the fortunes of which from 1923 onwards were guided mainly by economic conditions. It is time therefore to call a halt here, to have a look at the mechanical equipment of the early years. With MOM backing, there was no shortage of money, but there was a shortage of materials, and in the field of quarry machines it was not easy to obtain those of the required size, since O.I.was to operate on a scale much bigger than most existing quarries. As a result, the first two steam shovels were ordered from America in April 1918—a Marion X92 and a Bucyrus 103C. The Marion is listed in the plant register of May 1918, so had evidently already arrived, with the Bucyrus coming later. In 1919 two Wilson machines, a navvy and a crane, were hired from Topham, Jones & Railton Ltd; these were probably returned when replacements were obtained in the form of an 8-ton Ruston & Proctor navvy, a chain-bucket Whitaker excavator and a steam crane; the last came from the Inland Waterways & Docks Executive at Richborough, through the War Stores Disposals Board. By a coincidence, the first two locomotives had been ordered by the IW&DE but in the event were not required by them, and were offered as new to O.I. by the makers; and a good buy they proved to be. Two Manning Wardle locomotives were hired from the contractors also, but again were soon replaced by two locomotives from MOM Gretna Factory. A 20-ton steam navvy new from Ruston & Hornsby in 1920 completed the 'pre-Hickman' stock, much of which can have seen little use at the time. The wagon stock included 20 'dump cars', presumably for use on calcining clamps.

The rail track between quarries and main line railway was continually being modified throughout its life in accordance with traffic requirements, but the basic route was unaltered and can be described now, with changes to be noted as they occurred. The junction with the GWR down goods line was at 'Ironstone Mines Signal Box' (renamed 'Ironstone Branch Signal Box' in 1958) where the wagon storage sidings consisted of four parallel lines that converged near the junction and then swept away westwards in a set of marshalling sidings. From the same point a siding later ran at a lower level to the works of the Northern Aluminium Co Ltd, this branch being constructed in 1939. The ironstone line then ran parallel to the Oxford Canal for a short distance and was embanked to cross the Southam road by a girder bridge. About half way between the GWR and Southam Road the line crossed a trackway leading from the canal towpath towards Hardwick Farm; its purpose is unknown but it was deemed important enough to warrant a bridge over it. At the end of the straight stretch of mineral line by Pinhill Farm, one mile from the junction, were the original headquarters of the company rail system. On the north side of the line was the two-road locomotive shed of corrugated iron, with brick-built workshops alongside. South of the line were two calcining kilns, with sidings at a lower lever to accommodate wagons. On the hill overlooking the shed was a round concrete pond to collect water, which was passed through a softening plant for locomotive use.

Beyond the buildings the line entered a cutting, the south wall of which was stone-faced to carry on the higher level the siding to the tops of the kilns; from a chute at the end of this siding, the buckets of an aerial ropeway conveyed the ore to the kilns, which were emptied from the bottom into hopper wagons. The main line climbed steadily at successive gradients of 1 in 54, 1 in 60, 1 in 92 and 1 in 600, twisting continually.

Two miles from the junction, a skew brick arch (known as 'the German Bridge' because it was built largely by prisoner-of-war labour) carried the Banbury-Warwick road, which was altered in course for the purpose, over the line; the latter then reached more open country and enjoyed a falling gradient for half a mile or so before resuming the climb. Drayton Crossing was on this section, between the village and Drayton Lodge, then an embankment over a stream and, about three quarters of a mile further northwest, a level crossing (Moor Mill Crossing) with the lane to Hanwell. Just beyond here a short stretch of 1 in 35 was the steepest rise on the line. The road to Horley was crossed by a concrete arch and, a little way beyond, the rails reached Wroxton, the focal point of branches to the various quarries, on both sides of the level crossing with the Wroxton-Hornton road. Track was flat-bottomed, 56lbs per yard.

At the time of its construction it was from an engineering standpoint the finest ironstone railway in the country; the superior construction and maintenance almost of main line standards was called for by the intensive traffic the line was expected to bear and was manifested in a number of features not usually found on industrial tramways; quarter-mile posts and gradient posts, for example, and a railside telephone, giving the system an air of a main line mineral railway. Even more important, signal boxes were provided at the principal level crossings, Moor Mill and Wroxton, each provided with two signal levers and a wheel for opening the gates, of standard type; the Wroxton box also

Wroxton Quarries. The loop just above Drayton Crossing, on the original single line. (Eric Tonks)

had a third lever for operating a 'catch point', later discarded. Moor Mill box was of tarred brick, Wroxton box tarred brick with board top. The signals were made by McKenzie & Holland Ltd of Worcester but had been obtained, with the gates, from Saxby & Farmer in December

Wroxton Quarries. Signal on the Banbury side of Horley Crossing; the signal box can just be seen in the background. Note also the carriage at the top end of the siding. (Eric Tonks)

1921, so that initially the line was operated without these refinements—and the output in 1921–22 hardly justified them. The signal boxes and shunter's cabin at the GWR end had telephonic communication for the control of trains. Another early building at Wroxton was a black angular wooden shed that housed the gas engine to provide power for drilling; there was a Robey portable steam engine as reserve.

The contractors did not relinquish the site until 1921, and some of their men transferred to the ironstone company. The advent of the Hickman interest was the best piece of good fortune that came the way of O.I.; they rapidly became the biggest customer, by 1925 their quota exceeded that of Baldwins and Brymbo added together, and it may be presumed that they helped to shape policy at the quarries, whose production history started in earnest in 1923. Most of the ore was at first calcined, some in heaps and some in kilns; but a lot of trouble was experienced with the kilns, particularly from overheating, and the use of kilns (which dealt with 80 tons at a time) was discontinued in 1924

Wroxton Quarries. A number of roads in the Wroxton area were diverted to permit extraction of the ironstone beneath. The photograph shown the level crossing of the rail track to Friars Hill Quarry, with the new (diverted) road. Locomotive shed in centre of picture, offices extreme right. (B S C)

Wroxton Quarries. The crushing plant at Wroxton, probably soon after construction in the early 1930s. Ore brought in dumpcars from the quarries was tipped into the crusher at top right and discharged at lower left into wagons for transit to Banbury.

(B S C)

apparently, and the Board authorised dismantling of the kilns in April 1925—though they were still there until about 1940 and the bases visible at least until 1963. The calcine clamps (though O.I. always called them 'heaps') were operated in sets of three—one being built, one burning and one being taken away. From 1929 raw stone output considerably exceeded calcined and from 1932 all stone was sold in the raw state, as the extra labour of calcining cancelled the saving in freightage. It is recorded in the Minutes for 13th May 1935 that 'Heap 24 had been laid down about 4½ years before being lit on 26th Janury 1935, but burnt satisfactorily'. Crushing of stone was considered at first (Minute 21st February 1928) with the idea of making their own railway ballast from the bottom rock, and a small steam-operated machine was built, using the boiler of the Whitaker excavator; this was brought into use at the beginning of 1931 but was replaced by a much larger crusher, electrically operated, whereafter most of the stone, raw or calcinced, was crushed.

The 1920s were not easy times economically and the quarries were closed for various periods, like many others, eg. ten weeks October-December 1924, 1st July to 12th October 1925, 3rd May 1926 to January 1927, the last because of the General Strike. Production however steadily improved from 60,000 tons in 1923 to nearly ten

Wroxton Quarries. No. 5 TREASURER in the quarries, 14th June 1932. This locomotive was not at Wroxton long, being moved to Corby steelworks in January 1933.

(Dr J. R. Hollick)

times that in 1929, but with a drop in 1926; it then fell and from mid-1930 an increasing number of machines and locomotives were idle. From 1929 to 1934 the principal lessors allowed a reduction in royalties. In 1931/32 Hickmans was the only customer, Baldwins taking ore again in 1933 (all raw) until by 1936 the weekly output was over 20,000 tons. Demand continued to increase and at the outbreak of World War II the aim was for this to be doubled, from 15,000 to 30,000 tons per week, for which a further 160 men were to be employed.

A number of Italian prisoners-of-war worked here during the war, alongside the Polish contingent, occupying a series of huts near Pinhill Farm; locomotive enthusiasts had great difficulty in getting information because of this, quite apart from wartime considerations of security! Even after the war, production at a very high level was maintained, reaching a maximum of nearly 1¾ million tons in 1956. To accomplish this expansion there were continual changes in plant and quarry machines, while the opening of fresh quarrying areas required extensions to the railway layout, and new locomotives and rolling stock were called for.

The first quarry line is believed to have been laid in the direction of

Wroxton Quarries. Train approaching Horley Crossing, 14th June 1932—the steps of the signal box can be seen on the extreme right. The track was single at this time but there was ample space for another track. Locomotive is THE DEAN; several of the early locomotives were given the names of officers of the colleges from which the ground was leased.

(Dr J. R. Hollick)

'Langley Quarry', an ancient stone quarry in the angle between the Banbury-Stratford road and the road to Hornton, so that the area between here and Wroxton level crossing could be opened up; and a minute reference of 30th June 1925 to an ironstone face 1½ miles in length evidently refers to this. Shortly afterwards another quarry was opened, east of the Wroxton-Hornton lane and south of the minor lane running east from the level crossing; presumably there was a siding connection across the lane to the level crossing area. In both these quarries working is believed to have been clockwise, ie. northwards in the Langley Quarry and southwards in the other one. Detailed annual survey maps unfortunately seem not to have survived for this period, but we have those from 1934 on. In that year quarrying west of Wroxton on Christ Church land was proceeding steadily northwards, but leaving an 'island' surmounted by a water tower; while east of the level crossing Friars Hill Quarry was opened, working southwards toward the minor lane mentioned above. Production at both these quarries was in full swing at the outbreak of World War II and in both

151

cases permission was given to work straight across the line of lanes, which were temporarily closed and reopened after quarrying had passed beyond them; in each case again the replacement roads were on a different alignment—the minor lane south of Friars Hill being wholly sited to the south, apart from its eastern junction, and the section of the Wroxton-Horton road parallel to Ragnell Bottom was a straight chord in place of the original curve.

The main quarry line was extended by tunneling beneath the Hornton-Balscott lane (Dyke Lane) close to the old Langley Quarry, by a concrete bridge; known as Wroxton Heath Bridge, this was built by O.I. (minute 16th October 1936). This allowed the opening up of a large area to the west, and quarrying as far as the New Inn on the Stratford road commenced in 1940 and worked northwards; the Marion steam digger was a familiar sight to wartime travellers on the Stratford road. By 1945 quarrying had reached the bend in the lane to Ragnell Bottom, and early in 1951 the main line was extended parallel to the

Wroxton Quarries. The bridge under the Stratford road, made to open up the Balscott quarries, was designed to conform to the requirements of the local authority. The pictures shows an official inspection party about 1954.   (B S C)

Wroxton Quarries. Balscott Quarry, showing the fairly simple quarrying conditions; the overburden is shallow, and after extraction of the ironstone the ground is quickly returned to cultivation.

(B.G.S.)

main road, ending just beyond a level crossing with the minor road to Hornton Grounds. The ground beyond here to within a quarter mile of the Warwickshire border had been acquired in 1939, and was opened up in 1953. Plans to cross the main road in the vicinity of Upton House, which had been considered as long before as 1936, were revived, also to cross the county boundary (*Banbury Guardian* 22nd July 1954). During the late 1940s small quantities of stone were sold to a number of users outside the normal range — Round Oak, Lilleshall, Renishaw and Goldendale Ironworks, etc.

While these more remote extensions were going ahead, there were further developments nearer headquarters, the main one being the Balscott Quarries, reached in 1954 via a bridge under the Stratford road. This is (it still stands) a lofty structure faced with blocks of local stone shaped to give a smooth surface, and raising it above the utilitarian appearance of most quarry bridges; these refinements were in compliance with county council wishes, it is believed. Another area south of Friars Hill, was served by a short branch east of the Wroxton level crossing; this was a reopening in 1956 of workings abandoned since the mid-1920s. A side development of the postwar period was the building of a block of flats at Friars Hill, which were opened on 7th September 1952.

Wroxton Quarries. Balscott Quarry, with *D3*, a Ruston Bucyrus 43RB diesel dragline removing the thin overburden and a 100RB electric shovel loading dumpcars from the face, where the stone has been loosened by blasting. 10th June 1958. (B.G.S.)

Wroxton Quarries. One
of the lineside gradient
posts, a rare feature for an
industrial railway.
(Eric Tonks)

This expansion called for improvements to the railway system in addition to the purely quarry extensions. Originally the main line from Pinhill farm to Wroxton was single track apart from a crossing at Drayton, but the section of line from the Warwick Road bridge to Moor Mill level crossing was doubled and finally the whole distance in 1953.

The earlier track had flat-bottomed rail on earth ballast but later chaired track on ballast was mainly used, eg. the southern track of the main line, the extensions to Hornton Grounds and the Balscott branch, then some of the older lines were relaid with chaired track. The chairs were mostly secondhand, all pre-nationalisation railways being represented, and even LNWR: sleepers almost exclusively were wood, with a few steel ones, and ballast was obtained from the quarries. Flat-bottomed rail continued to be used for points in most cases. It is interesting to note that on the main line right-hand working was in force, presumably because the crusher was on the south side and left-hand working would have involved crossing over the 'up' line every time a train left. Presumably at the time crushing was introduced, a manned cabin was installed at Friars Hill, in telephonic communication with Moor Mill signal box.

The locomotive allocation of course increased with production requirements. In 1923 there were six, and in the years 1924-35 the strength remained between seven and nine, the numbers not necessarily reflecting output; while nine were on the strength in 1929-32 there were for most of this time only three or four in use. When trade began to pick up in the mid-thirties, locomotive usage increased,

Wroxton Quarries. No. 2 LORD NORTH at Pinhill 14th August 1938. Note the disused calcine kilns at the rear. (E. J. Jones)

and there was a further change brought about by the introduction of ore crushing. The crusher was located on the south side of the line east of the Wroxton level crossing, on part of the old Friars Hill quarry site, and called for modification of the layout. 'Dumpcars' that had hitherto been used on the calcine heaps (their normal duty in ironstone quarries) were used to bring ore to the crusher; trains were pulled from the quarries and then propelled up the gradient to sidings level with the top of the crusher, into which the contents were tipped, the crushed stone being discharged at the bottom into wagons (mostly hoppers or iron ore tipplers) standing on a siding at the main line level and run by gravity under the chute. There was therefore more locomotive work at Wroxton, and in the mid-1930s one locomotive (*Phyllis* usually) was kept there at all times. In 1936-38 three more locomotives were purchased, all four-wheelers, purely for quarry traffic and all stationed at Wroxton; they were housed in a long single-road corrugated iron shed with concrete floor and inspection pit, close to the west side of the level crossing, and capable of holding five locomotives. Thus came about the subdivision of locomotive duties that characterised the O.I. rail system in its mature form. Up to 1935 all locomotives (including six new from the makers) were six-wheelers

Wroxton Quarries. The locomotive sheds at Pinhill Farm, serving the main line. The original two-road shed is on the right, workshops in centre and later (1938) shed at left. The huts at the rear were living quarters for ex-prisoners of war. 22nd March 1965.   (F. A. Blencowe)

Wroxton Quarries. The locomotive sheds at Pinhill Farm, with the main line to the quarries at left; coaling stage; workshops (small dark building); and main shed, 22nd March 1965.   (F. A. Blencowe)

Wroxton Quarries. Peckett locomotive MAUD pushes a train of twelve loaded dumpcars to the crusher 1st September 1964.   (P. H. Groom)

apart from three four-wheelers acquired from the constituent companies in 1923-25; the 'main line' from Banbury to Wroxton required locomotives with greater hauling power, as well as tank and bunker capacity, and the small engines were not much used except for yard shunting. The introduction of stone crushing brought about the segregation of locomotives into six-wheelers based at Pinhill Farm shed for working the main line, and four-wheelers based at Wroxton for working between quarries and crusher.

While the main line remained unaltered apart from completion of doubling, the quarry lines extended further and further away, hence the allocation of locomotives at Wroxton increased faster than Pinhill Farm; the original shed at the latter held four locomotives but was extended rearwards about 1929 to hold six and an ancillary single-road shed of corrugated iron for two locomotives was built in 1938. At Wroxton, the locomotive stock increased to six during World War II and a shed for four locomotives, similar to the first but on the north side and a little further from the level crossing, was brought into use in 1953 and its capacity doubled by lengthening in July 1957, when nine locomotives was the average allocation. A locomotive repair shop

Wroxton Quarries. The 'Duty Board' on Wroxton signal box. *E1, W1* etc are quarry machine numbers; *BETTY* etc are locomotive names serving the machines. The working faces were identified by the machines working there. The milkman had just called! 7th August 1967.   (M. J. Leah)

alongside the old shed at Wroxton was built in 1958. In the postwar (World War II) years the sight of a four-wheeler at Pinhill Farm was almost unknown apart from *Phyllis*, abandoned on a siding alongside the shed, and usually occupied by discarded locomotives; *Phyllis* was used as a snowplough during the hard winter of 1947. At Wroxton it was four-wheelers in general, with perhaps one or two six-wheelers (the 15ins. cylinder ones mainly) up for occasional use or repair. This segregation led to another distinctive feature in naming policy, the new six-wheelers being given boys' names and new four-wheelers girls' names; this is discussed in more detail below.

Increase in locomotive stock was paralleled by a similar increase in quarry machines, which had been introduced at O.I. quarries from the start. In all some twenty machines were used, half of them steam, a form of power to which O.I. remained faithful later than most quarry operators, few of whom purchased new steam machines after 1930. As the overburden was nowhere deep, there were none of the huge draglines that were so prominent a feature of the ironstone quarries further east; but what they lacked in size they made up in variety, and the system of coding, under which each machine was designated by a letter and a number, was unique.

In the early days ore was despatched to the ironworks in wagons supplied by the owners. Those used by Alfred Hickman Ltd were either wooden wagons of normal type or 20-ton steel hoppers, painted light brown and with the owner's name in white; in later years they were lettered Stewarts & Lloyds Ltd, but still in light brown livery. Baldwins and Brymbo doubtless supplied their own wagons, probably of similar type. These wagons worked on the main line between Wroxton and the GWR. In the post-World War II years, BR hoppers or iron ore tipplers were standard. Dumpcars (in some early correspondence referred to as 'tipper cars' or 'American cars') were used from the start in connection with calcining, when they were loaded at the working face and emptied at the calcine kilns or heaps; later these plied between face and crusher. The numbers of these wagons increased greatly as output rose.

Locomotives

In all thirty three steam locomotives are known to have worked on the system, nineteen of them new from the makers. The first two locomotives were sturdy-looking six-coupled side tanks by Hudswell

Wroxton Quarries. SIR THOMAS, doyen of the Oxfordshire Ironstone fleet, and the only steam locomotive to be preserved. The three engines of this class were very well liked, and were a standard Hudswell Clarke design. The photo was taken on 19th April 1960.

(J. L. Brown)

Wroxton Quarries. THE PRESIDENT is the same class as SIR THOMAS and LORD NORTH, but was named some time after arrival new; the nameplates were supplied by Hunslet Engine Co instead of by the makers, Hudswell Clarke. Photo 4th November 1961.

(M. J. Lee)

Clarke; as already noted, they had been ordered by the Inland Waterways & Docks Executive but were no longer required by them and thus came to O.I. as new locomotives in 1918. For the start of production two locomotives were hired from the contractors and two purchased from the Ministry of Munitions Gretna factory. Of these last, some mystery surrounds the identity of *Nancy*, which has been assumed to be HE 356, but the records are conflicting; in O.I. records *Nancy* is shown as Hudswell Clarke 450, which was a 5ft. gauge locomotive supplied to Estonia — but, on the other hand, Hunslet 450 was also at MOM Gretna; so *Nancy* may be HE 450, as the known history of HE 356 appears to rule out this number. She was cut up before any enthusiasts could establish identity from close examination. Her companion, No. 14, also had a comparatively short life, unlike the majority of Manning Wardles, and ceased work in January 1931, when she was placed in the siding by the shed at Pinhill Farm until cut up in 1938. During the lean years of the early 'twenties three 0-4-0ST were supplied by the constituent companies of O.I., but they were not well suited for the mainly long-distance haulage the system required. One more new locomotive was obtained, a further example of the highly

Wroxton Quarries. Most Manning Wardles had long lives, but the Oxfordshire Ironstone example did not: as a contractor's engine she had probably done her fair share of hard work. MW 1749 is shown out of use at Pinhill shed 2nd August 1936.

(K. Cooper/IRS Collection)

Wroxton Quarries. GWEN, one of the first purely quarry engines. She was the last locomotive to be given a number as well as a name, later locomotives bought new being given names only. Note the unusual curved maker's plate on the sandpot.

(K. Cooper/IRS Collection)

successful 'IWD' type; she came in 1923, but seems not to have borne the name *The President*. Plates of this name were ordered from Hunslet Engine Co Ltd in June 1926, probably when *The Dean* was ordered; this explains why *The President* is in non-serif Hunslet-type lettering while *Sir Thomas* and *Lord North* are in the serif lettering adopted by Hudswell Clarke.

There followed a long series of locomotives new from the makers, including three 0-4-0ST for purely quarry work up at Wroxton; up to this time the new locomotives had been given numbers and names but after *No. 6* names only were applied and in later years a system was adopted in which boys' names were used for 'main line' locomotives and girls' names for locomotives on quarry work, which in practice meant respectively six- and four-wheelers. Existing names were not altered unless they conflicted with this ruling, eg. *Joan* (P 1981) became *John* in August 1957 with a pair of new plates supplied locally by The Hub Ironworks of Chipping Norton. On the other hand, *Hellidon* became *Graham* in 1955, seemingly because the former name was disliked (it is of a village near Charwelton, where the locomotive had

Wroxton Quarries. Peckett JOHN was originally JOAN, but changed sex when it was decided to restrict girls names to quarry locomotives. New plates were cast at The Hub Ironworks, Chipping Norton. May 1958.   (G. Alliez, courtesy B. D. Stoyel)

Wroxton Quarries. When the diesels started arriving, the nameplates of many of the steamers were removed for transfer to the diesels. BARABEL's driver made his own wooden replacements. 1st September 1964.   (P. H. Groom)

Wroxton Quarries. Hudswell Clarke locomotive BETTY in nice condition outside the old shed at Wroxton, with stores at rear. Note the extended bunker, as fitted to this locomotive and sister BARABEL.

(B S C)

worked). The boys' and girls' names all have some reference to company officials or their families, the unusual *Barabel*, for example, being the name of the wife of A. C. Stewart, Chairman of Stewarts & Lloyds Ltd 1945-64.

Whatever the merits of this classification, boys' and girls' names are too commonly used on industrial locomotives to generate much interest and we confess to disappointment that the opportunity was not taken to use local names, eg. *Edge Hill, Hornton* etc. The most interesting names at O.I. were the older ones with their historical associations—*Sir Thomas, Lord North*—and those alluding to college dignitaries, such as *The Dean. Basic* derives from O.I.'s telegraphic address of 'Basic Banbury' and *Sir Charles* (Wright) was Chairman of O.I. 1936-38/45-49. This is a purely personal viewpoint; but few would complain about the choice of livery, which was crimson lake (referred to in O.I. shops as LMS red) with various linings. The Pecketts had black edged yellow, and lake connecting rods; *The Dean* was similar, and the rest of the Hunslets likewise except that the rods were red; the Hudswell Clarkes had a surrounding black margin, edged scarlet and a yellow line, and the Sentinel *Phyllis* a plain yellow line. All looked very smart and the standard of cleanliness was commendably high. Some of the secondhand locomotives retained their various styles of painting, eg. *Noel*, green; *Phyllis*, gamboge lined black, a most unusual livery; *Newlay*, green lined black edged yellow, with red rods and green wheels; *Byfield No. 2*, green lined black edged yellow (outside) and red(inside). *Barnsley*, obtained on loan from Hudswell Clarke pending the delivery of HC 1868/1869, was black, lined red. This last livery also applied to *Hellidon/Graham*, but 'she' was repainted in 1958 in the standard lake but with a lining of black edged cream, which was also applied to the wheel centres, and had red rods.

Number *303* was black with red rods but was repainted in standard O.I. livery. *Jean* was also given standard O.I. livery, and nameplates with straight letters. The Manning Wardle had no name but carried *No. 14* of a previous owner on the saddle tank, and had the standard O.I. livery of lake lined black edged yellow, probably by coincidence.

Nameplates were of brass with red background, only *Newlay* having a painted name (yellow edged red). Serif lettering was the rule for the Pecketts and early Hudswell Clarkes, non-serif for the Hunslets and the three last Hudswell Clarkes *Mary, Betty, Barabel*, and the Sentinel. The locomotives were of the makers standard designs, though individual points of interest may be noted, eg. the curved maker's plates on *Gwen's* sandboxes; and the increased bunker capacity of *Betty* and *Barabel* as compared with *Mary*, to cope with the longer hauls between quarries and Wroxton. Locomotives were fitted with combination couplings—buckeye for handling dumpcars, link for BR wagons.

The locomotive foreman in later years was Bill Rogers, a steam enthusiast through and through, and in whose genial charge a very high standard of locomotive maintenance was achieved; and with the intimate knowledge of his fleet, Bill would be happy to discuss the relative merits of the various types. The favourites undoubtedly were the original trio of Hudswell Clarke side tanks, which were free-steaming consistent performers; the Pecketts in comparison were less popular—less free-steaming and heavy on maintenance—but they were cheaper than the HCs and HEs, which is presumably why the company bought them. They were good hard-slogging engines all the same, Bill told Mick Lee, and the crews got the best out of them. Bill had loads of reminiscences of course, eg. of the locomotives enveloped in steam as they charged the cally banks with rakes of loaded dumpcars. *Allan* had an unfortunate accident when 'he' had been on the line about twelve months; coming down with a loaded train over Drayton passing loop, the point blades kicked over after the locomotive had cleared them, derailing the first wagon and then others. The coupling between locomotive and wagon held and the engine pulled on its side, facing Banbury. The driver stuck to his post and hung on to the regulator and reversing lever, which saved him from serious injury, and he escaped from the cabside, which was open to the sky, by climbing on the regulator. The latter opened with his weight and *Allan* was set in motion on its side; there was an almighty roar from the chimney and the surrounding fields were deluged with a mixture of steam, hot water and soot until the boiler was empty. The line was blocked for two days while the GWR breakdown unit was brought in to right *Allan*, still facing Banbury. It was hauled back to the shed and Bill and his gang had the job of turning it round a bit at a time on steel plates; they thought they would never finish it. The dent in the left hand tank was hammered out but *Allan* retained the scars ever after (notes from Mick Lee).

Graham, which turned the scale at around 50 tons, was considered by Alex Mackay, the General Manager, too heavy for general duty over the main line, and she was restricted to working between Pinhill and

Wroxton Quarries. ALLAN suffered a derailment, falling on its side, and though returned to full working order, carried the scars ever since. 28th August 1961.

(K. Cooper/IRS Collection)

the BR exchange sidings; but this ruling was later relaxed, without apparent detriment to the track.

After all the wonderful work achieved by their fleet of standard locomotives it is surprising that the penultimate steam locomotive purchased new proved to be a disaster from the start. When the purchase of a 200hp Sentinel was mooted, Bill Rogers was sent to East Moors Steelworks to see Sentinels in action, but he was not much impressed by them and advised Mr Young, then General Manager, accordingly; however, the machine was bought and put through its paces, taking an empty train up to Wroxton with *Spencer* pottering gently behind in case of accidents. *Phyllis* stalled a couple of times on the steeper gradients and was very slow throughout, and the journey ended with *Spencer* pushing the lot up to Friars Hill. A downhill run was better for time, but the braking power left a lot to be desired. As a result she was confined to quarry duty—and not much of that! She was used occasionally up to February 1959, then put in the shed while the manufacturers tried modifications. A further trial in April 1960 led

Wroxton Quarries. The 200 hp Sentinel steam locomotive PHYLLIS was not often in steam but Mick Rhodes managed to take this photograph on 15th September 1956, soon after delivery. She is about to push a train of loaded dumpcars up the crusher sidings. Behind her is the old Wroxton locomotive shed with LORD NORTH out of use.

Wroxton Quarries. Disused locomotives were sometimes stored at the side of Pinhill shed. The Bagnall PHYLLIS is shown here, about 1954. (F. Jones)

to sporadic use but in December 1960 *Phyllis* was laid aside for good. Sentinel steam locomotives were excellent machines for yard work, and very economical when handled correctly, but not really suitable for the conditions obtaining at O.I.

This did not diminish O.I.'s faith in steam, though, and on 19th November 1958 they took delivery of *Frank*, the very last steam locomotive to be supplied to the ironstone industry, which in general retained steam later than most industries. This tardy awareness of the advantages of diesel locomotives had its own reward, as by the time the company seriously considered the matter, a great deal of progress in diesel locomotive design had been made, and the locomotives tested in the field. O.I. took no chances and at least six designs were tested in 1960 and 1961. Hunslet supplied a 350hp 0-6-0DM (4551) for main line work and a smaller four-coupled one (not identified) for quarry work. Ruston & Hornsby sent their 287hp demonstration 0-4-0DH (437368) of class LSSH, in 1960, and a 200hp 0-4-0DE (433676) in 1961.

170

Wroxton Quarries. FRANK, Hunslet 3872 of 1958, was the last steam locomotive built for Oxfordshire Ironstone, but similar in design to a number of others that had given fine service. She is here photographed 7th August 1959 in the standard maroon livery. (K. Cooper/IRS Collection)

Yorkshire Engine selected a 0-6-0DE for trial, and Andrew Barclay are also believed to have sent a machine. The Ruston diesel-electric was considered the best and an order was just about to be placed when Thos. Hill asked if they could demonstrate a Sentinel diesel-hydraulic. It says much for their representative's persuasive powers that the company agreed, considering the pup they had been sold in the shape of *Phyllis*, languishing unused and unwanted in the shed at Wroxton. However, agree they did and 0-4-0DH 10072 was put through its paces, with results better than so far obtained; slowness on the main line was a drawback that the manufacturers could overcome and the first new locomotive arrived in December 1961, allocated to Wroxton shed and working the new Alkerton Pit. She was painted crimson lake with two yellow lines and bore no name (simply referred to as 'the diesel') and the success of the experiment was demonstrated by the purchase of a

171

Wroxton Quarries. Delight of the locomotive enthusiast. The long loco shed at Wroxton, with engines 'sizzling' after the day's work. At front is THE BURSAR. 4th November 1961. (S. A. Leloux)

similar locomotive twelve months later. She was painted lake lined black edged with yellow but again carried no name; these two engines were referred to as 'Diesel No. 1' and 'Diesel No.2'.

The decision was then taken to dieselize the locomotive fleet completely by the bulk purchase of eleven more locomotives, starting with 10165, which arrived in September 1964, with nameplates *Joan* from the recently withdrawn steam locomotive. The Wroxton stock was replaced first, completed with the delivery of *Jean* in January 1965; and a reconditioned boiler for *Gwen* was never fitted. Steam continued to be used on the main line for another six months, partly it was said so that some useful work could be obtained from the five locomotives recently fitted with vacuum brakes, but probably because the specification of the Sentinels for main line work was under discussion. Instead of using six-coupled locomotives, it was decided to standardize on the 311hp 0-4-0DH type; the quarry locomotives were lighter than the standard design — 30 ton for the first three, 31 ton for the other five — while the main line locomotives were of Sentinel's

Wroxton Quarries. An outside view of the long locomotive shed taken three years later, 1st September 1964, when the steam locomotives were rapidly being displaced by 'Sentinel' diesels. THE BURSAR lies outside, discarded, behind her a row of loaded dumpcars, and the long shed. Note the difference between the old portion to the right and the newer section to the left.   (P. H. Groom)

standard 40 tons, such that the axle load was the same as the six-coupled steamers. The quarry engines also had a lower gearbox ratio to reduce the starting tractive effort in line with the weight reduction, whilst retaining the maximum speed. There was little external difference in the two kinds, which however were distinguished by a continuation of the policy of naming the quarry locomotives after girls and main line locomotives after boys, using nameplates from former steam locomotives. In all twenty two steamers were replaced by thirteen diesels, eight in the quarries and five on the main line. Some at least of the diesels received 'Gloucester' couplings from steam locomotives.

The changeover from steam to diesel proceeded smoothly as a result of the lengthy tests in service of the first two diesels; but it was not entirely popular with the locomen, many of whom had spent their working lives with steam and missed the familiar and friendly

173

atmosphere it always seemed to engender. In the last years the steamers became increasingly shabby, in marked contrast to past practice, and the anonymity imposed by removal of nameplates (for application to diesels, or simply for safekeeping) was deplored in itself; steam locomotives have an individual character (*Lord North*, it was said, was never as good an engine as *Sir Thomas* or *The President*, for some unaccountable reason) and the loss of the nameplates was felt far beyond the bare patch on the tanks. The driver of *Barabel* indeed went so far as to make little wooden nameplates to compensate. These sentiments were echoed by the railway enthusiasts, of course, who flocked to the system to record the last days of steam. The 'long shed' at Wroxton had often elicited awed comments at the sight of eight assorted steam locomotives, half of them still 'sizzling' after the days' work; five gleaming Sentinels had an atmosphere too, from their very uniformity, but the smoke and steam were missing.

The steam locomotives were disposed of mainly to James Friswell, the Banbury scrap dealer, who cut them up on the spot, or to Cohens, who took them by road to their yard at Cransley and cut them up there—amongst them *Phyllis*, not ten years old. One however was sold for preservation—*No. 1 Sir Thomas*, the obvious choice. She last worked 8th July 1965 and then was put into store in Pinhill workshops. There was talk of displaying her on a piece of track on the lawn in front of the offices at Wroxton, but this was not done, but Bill Rogers lavished on her his continuing loving care, including a monthly run to keep the motion in trim, so that when she did go for preservation she was in fine condition, and as near to original form as possible. At our suggestion, the plates of *Lord North* were presented to the Fairleigh Dickinson University of New Jersey, USA, the new owners of Wroxton Abbey, with whom the name had so long an association. They asked for a photograph of the locomotive to go with the plates, but Mr Young did not possess one; so *Sir Thomas* was taken out, the nameplate on one side temporarily replaced and the maker's plate altered to conform to that of *Lord North* by a few strokes of red paint! The numberplate on the wall however is not that formerly on *Lord North*—as revealed by the incongruity in the style of lettering—but from *Joan* (AE 1822); the wrong 'No. 2' must have been taken from the stores. But what matter—they are both worth saving.

174

Wroxton Quarries. SIR THOMAS on the main line, 8th June 1965, passing Horley Crossing (crossing gate post can just be seen at right). Note signal for up line to left.
(Ivo Peters)

Quarry Machines

Oxfordshire Ironstone purchased 22 quarry machines, half of them steam, the rest diesel or electric power. At the time of construction, 1918, large machines of British manufacture were difficult to obtain and two steam shovels were imported from America, a Bucyrus and a Marion. Two machines by J. H. Wilson were hired from the contractors in 1919 and then four machines were acquired secondhand. One of them, a steam crane that came from the Inland Waterways & Docks Executive, Richborough, was built by Newton, Bean & Mitchell Ltd of Bradford after World War I; a decidedly rare make, and certainly the only known example in the ironstone fields. She carried plates 'I W & D E No. 165' and 'Richboro' Port No. 47' and had a 35-foot lattice jib. Rare make or not, she proved a very useful unit and outlasted all the other steam machines; she last worked in April 1961 and a few years later was rebuilt with a diesel engine by Smith Rodley of Leeds and on closure was sold in this guise to a local plant dealer, Peter Court, in whose premises she remained in 1982. The other machines were more orthodox; nonetheless, a few mysteries remain, even with the great volume of information available. One was a Whitaker C type chain-bucket steam excavator, purchased in 1919, from whom it is not stated; she seems not to have been very much used and in 1930 the engine and boiler were transferred to the No. 2 Crushing Plant. Her contemporary 20-ton Ruston Proctor steam navvy was however an extremely popular machine, but her makers' number and origin are not recorded; named *Jimmy*, she was frequently mentioned in the files and was working in World War II, last being recorded late in 1945. A similar 20-ton Ruston Proctor was acquired from Alfred Hickman's Sydenham Pits after they closed down, and arrived as *No. 1*; but—presumably as a gesture to *Jimmy*—was given a name—what else but *Syd*?

These assorted machines were more than adequate for the lean operating years of the 1920s but in 1929 when trade picked up—as it turned out, only temporarily—a further Marion 92 shovel was ordered; this was similar to the previous machine with the exception of the boiler, which was built in England by Marshall Sons & Co Ltd, of Gainsborough, who are believed also to have supplied a new boiler for the older Marion. Thereafter standard Ransomes & Rapier and Ruston-Bucyrus machines gradually took over. The first two Ransomes & Rapiers were 480 type draglines and were steam-powered, the last of

Wroxton Quarries. Oxfordshire Ironstone Co Ltd had two Marion steam shovels, the first coming from America in 1918, and the second, with boiler supplied by Marshalls of Gainsborough, in 1930. The photograph shows the interesting mechanical arrangements for shovelling. (BSC)

their class to be so in the ironstone fields; built in 1935 and 1937, they were called *Dragline No. 1* and *Dragline No. 2* respectively but were later used as shovels. Number 2 was supplied with a shovel end as an 'extra' when new and No. 1 converted to a digger in 1944, when overburden removal became the province of Ruston-Bucyrus diesels; they were later renamed *Rapier No. 1* and *Rapier No. 2; Rapier No. 3* of 1937 was a diesel dragline for removing overburden, but she seems to have been too small for the work and was disposed of at the end of the war. *Rapier No. 4* of 1939 was a larger machine, a 490 electric shovel (plus dragline gear) and from then onwards Ruston-Bucyrus became the order of the day. They were standard 43RB, 54RB and 100RB types and the most interesting feature was their identification by means of a coding letter and number. Interested enthusiasts noted

177

Wroxton Quarries. One of the Marion shovels out of use—probably at the quarry close to the Stratford road where she worked for many years, including World War II. About 1950. (B S C)

these symbols painted on the cabsides as they worked away in the fields and on the 'duty board' exhibited on the Wroxton signal box; some presumed that the coding referred to the working faces but in fact it was the other way round—the working faces adopted the codes of the loading shovels. This seems to have been a longstanding practice, as there is a reference in the minute of 26th July 1927 to the 'Ruston Working Face'.

In practice the system was not as simple as might have been expected, as the coding was altered piecemeal as new machines were acquired. In 1941/42/43 one each of machines 100RB, 43RB and 54RB were purchased; the first (RB 5896) was referred to as 'RB Electric Shovel' and the others (RB 6995/6997), both diesel, by their type designations. In 1948 however a second 54RB (RB 8647) was bought and given the name *Winston*, identification enough; at the same time the 100RB was christened *E1*, a readily understandable coding. Three years later, in 1951, a further electric 100RB (RB 12374) and a 43RB diesel (RB 14060) were purchased, the former becoming *E2* and the latter *D3*, though there were already three other diesels in

Wroxton Quarries. Ransomes & Rapier Ltd built very few quarry machines driven by steam, but Oxfordshire Ironstone had two 480 draglines of this type. The picture shows one removing overburden.

(B S C)

service, and it is here that the complexities start.

Winston retained its name but in the books became *Winston 1*, while the older 54RB (RB 6997) became *Winston 2*, shortened in the following year to *W1* and *W2*. In this year, 1953, a third 43RB (15952) arrived, labelled *D1*, while the original 43RB (6995) became *D4*, still leaving *D3* blank; a third 54RB (15578) was called *Winston* (or *W)3*. By this time the inherent simplicity of the coding scheme was becoming blurred by inconsistencies, but this was regularised in 1956. The 100RBs retained *E1* and *E2*, the 54RBs, formerly *W1-3*, became *B1-3*, and the 43RBs *D1-3* (formerly *D1, D3, D4*). The last machine, purchased in that year, became *B4*, and was a 71B. In a letter dated 8th November 1955 to Ruston-Bucyrus, Mr Young asked for a machine between the 100RB and 54RB, combining the capacity for dealing with hard rock of the former with the easier manoeuvrability of the latter; the 71B met these requirements but as it was not available from Lincoln at the time, a machine was imported from the associated company in America. The machines were painted in the standard crimson lake colour, unlined, with the code letters and numbers in white characters.

The duties of these machines are recorded in the log books and were typical of general ironstone practice, eg. at Balscott twelve empty wagons were taken to the East Face and all loaded by machine *E1*; but at the West Face the rake was divided into two sets of six, one being filled by *W1*, the other by *B3*, as a significant difference in the ore at the two ends of the face called for segregation at the crusher.

Wagons

Ore was transported from the O.I. premises to various ironworks in wagons supplied by the latter, in the normal manner, but right from the start there were 'internal' wagons for use in conjunction at first with calcining and later with ore-crushing. These wagons were of the familiar 'dumpcar' type, and the size of the O.I. system led to a very large allocation of these wagons. The first 20 were 12-ton wagons supplied by the Bristol & South Wales Wagon Co Ltd, numbered 1-20, and were sometimes referred to as 'American cars', but later the more familiar 'dumpcars' or 'tipper cars' was used for those supplied by Gloucester Railway Carriage and Wagon Co Ltd, which held 15 tons, and were numbered in order:-

31- 70	supplied 1924–25
71- 90	supplied 1936
91-130	supplied 1937
131-180	supplied 1940
181-225	supplied 1957

In the first 20 years there were four braked cars; in the later ones there were five braked per set of fourteen. Oxfordshire Ironstone also bought some ore hoppers from the same builder, 20 in 1939 and 42 in 1941. In the early 1930s 50 cars were loaned to Corby.

More interesting were the 'odds and ends' of wagon stock associated with the length of line; one feature was the 'workman's train' consisting of a locomotive and a passenger vehicle running from Pinhill Farm to Wroxton in the morning, and back at close of work; on the homeward journey no stops were made, the men dropping off at the most convenient point en route until an empty train reached the locomotive shed. A

Wroxton Quarries. One of the 'dumpcars' used for transporting the ironstone from quarry to crusher. The body is centrally pivoted and secured in position by chains, and is arranged for side-tipping in either direction. Oxfordshire Ironstone had some 200 of these wagons. Photograph 4th November 1961.   (G. H. Starmer)

Wroxton Quarries. Avonside JOAN, showing the buckeye coupling for dumpcars, as well as buffers. 28th August 1961. (K. Cooper/IRS Collection)

Wroxton Quarries. Old coach body off the track, with Horley bridge in the background, 25th February 1956. (Eric Tonks)

Wroxton Quarries. Before the brakevans were acquired, the workmen travelled in vans, as the one shown here on 25th February 1965. (Eric Tonks)

Wroxton Quarries. Workman's train with GRAHAM and ex-GWR brakevan 4th November 1961, waiting to take quarrymen down towards Banbury. Note signal, offices, signal box, level crossing gate. (S. A. Leloux)

number of vehicles served in this capacity; an elderly North London Railway four-wheeled luggage van seems to have been the first, and when this was pensioned off, it stood on an isolated piece of track close to Moor Mill level crossing, and finally the body was dumped by the bridge near Horley, and the frame used as a flat wagon at Pinhill sheds. Its early history is uncertain but it carried a faded No. 20 on its panels and 31584 inside the door, and it may have come from the War Department. It was replaced in service by an ex-LNER (originally North British Railway) van.

This closed van was fitted with wooden seats and painted orange. Finally ex-GWR brakevan 17908 (Swindon 1913) was purchased in 1958, also painted orange. When vacuum-braked operation was installed in 1964, seven more former GWR brakevans were obtained, as follows:

1	GWR No. 17898 Swindon 1914
2	GWR No. 68564 Swindon 1924
3	GWR No. 68642 Swindon 1924
4	GWR No. 68684 Swindon 1924
5	GWR No. 68619 Swindon 1924
6	GWR No. 68669 Swindon 1924
7	GWR No. 68677 Swindon 1924

These too were painted orange, with the running number carried on a red panel at the rear end. The original brakevan continued in service as the 'workman's train' and was not used on the ore trains.

There was a miscellaneous set of wagons used internally. These included three-plank wooden wagons numbered 4-8, 10/13 –16, all secondhand of course, from the LMSR (four at least ex-Midland Railway) and elsewhere, painted black and used for carrying coal and ashes. There was also a closed van, possibly ex- North British Railway, used by platelayers; a water tank plated 'Ince Wagon & Ironworks Co Ltd L.N.W.R 1917'; and two flat wagons derived from 'Gloucester' dumpcars. Another of the latter had a corrugated iron hut mounted on the frame (described by Roger West as a 'henhouse' type) and used as a tool van. Finally there was an ex-BR (SR) well wagon with one end cut off and mounted on a bogie, used for carrying heavy machinery. A snowplough was kept for use in the appropriate conditions. A 'gang trolley' was purchased in March 1935, but few details have survived. Thanks to Mike Rhodes for information on some of these vehicles.

The final years

Maximum output was achieved in 1956 and declined afterwards, resulting in a three-day operating week by 1959; and thereon, while production was geared to a fluctuating demand, the rule was for short-time working. In hindsight, the writing could be seen on the wall; but at the time, the possibility of closure seems never to have been considered, and there were many changes in quarry and railway operation—for the two were very closely bound up—in the early 1960s. Some were introduced for reasons of safety, others for economy, but all forward-looking, making the system always interesting to the enthusiast and giving no hint that all was suddenly to come to an end. On a normal working day there were six or seven trips to Wroxton each with fourteen empty hoppers, returning with the same number full; the journey time was 20-25 minutes between Wroxton and Pinhill Farm. Five locomotives were in steam for these main line duties.

The locomotives faced uphill, always with the chimney next to the train, which was propelled to Wroxton and hauled back—a disappointing feature for photographers. This however changed in April 1963, following the purchase of six brakevans from Swindon, which enabled locomotives to haul the trains up to Wroxton. This policy was introduced after a fatal accident to a Polish quarryman on 8th January 1963; he was riding on the brake pole lodged in the wagon frame—the rule forbidding this practice was commonly ignored—as the train went towards Banbury, and, as he turned to wave to a group of men who were clearing snow from the track, his feet caught on a pile of snow and he was thrown under the wheels. A further reason was the introduction of vacuum brake working, following the advice of BR that the provision of about four brake-fitted wagons per train, plus a brakevan, would enable longer trains to be handled in safety. In October and November 1963 five of the main line locomotives (*Basic, Sir Charles, Spencer, Frank, Sir Thomas*) were vacuum fitted, and the system worked quite well once the right proportion of braked wagons was supplied by BR. The trains then usually consisted of sixteen wagons plus brakevan; the vacuum-fitted tipplers were painted red.

The reference to Polish workmen should be explained; there was a sizeable Polish community arising from men who were drafted here early in World War II, and who chose to settle here; a series of wooden huts close to Pinhill locomotive shed housed a group of them.

The introduction of diesel locomotives was another step

185

Wroxton Quarries. Probably Alkerton Quarry, with a 100RB shovel loading a train of fourteen 27-ton tipplers in the charge of a Sentinel diesel locomotive. Here again, the overburden is light and the effect on the landscape minimal. (B S C)

Wroxton Quarries. A scenic point near the Warwickshire border; MARY takes a loaded train across the trackway to Hornton Grounds, April 1964.   (M. J. Leah)

forward—economically speaking—and was carried out over 1962-65 to the total elimination of steam working, giving the railway a more efficient, if less appealing, image. In 1962 Spencer Works in South Wales commenced taking uncrushed stone, presumably on grounds of economy; apart from not having to be crushed, the stone could be loaded at the quarry face into 27-ton tipplers and taken direct to the furnaces. Some stone however was still crushed, and a 'mule', built and installed by their own workshop force, moved wagons through the crusher without requiring a locomotive.

There were continuing extensions of the rail system as quarrying was prosecuted further afield; the Balscott quarries, it will be recalled, were opened up in 1954, the branch to them taken under the Stratford road via a new bridge; a further bridge under the same road in the vicinity of the New Inn was completed in 1958 and enabled the Alkerton quarries to be developed. Finally, the Hornton grounds extension was taken up to the county boundary. There were no further major extensions, but there was continual improvement in equipment. In 1961 red and green colour light signals were placed on each side of Balscott bridge, where the curve in the approaches from each direction precluded a clear view; similar signals were introduced at Wroxton,

Wroxton Quarries. Moor Mill signal box, with the earlier wooden crossing gates. A murderer gave himself up to the signalman here! (Eric Tonks)

though the semaphores were not removed. The new signals controlled the approaches from Balscott, Hornton and the crusher. In 1962 new level-crossing gates of tubular steel with wire mesh, painted white with a red spot, replaced the old ones both at Wroxton and Moor Mill. A new trailing siding and crossover was put in between Friars Hill and

Wroxton Quarries. Moor Mill Crossing, Horley. BASIC with loaded train 20th April 1965. Note vacuum brake, fitted in later years. Note also the observation post for inspecting empty wagons on the way up to the quarries. (S. A. Leloux)

Wroxton Quarries. BETTY heading towards Wroxton from Alkerton Quarry, 7th August 1967. The line was single under Dyke Lane bridge, from which this view was taken. The extent of excavated fields is clear from the lowered ground level, as compared with the Stratford road on far left. (M. J. Leah)

Horley bridge. Close by the signal box at Moor Mill, an inspection platform was erected; this feature was common to many modern ironstone systems, the object being to inspect the empty wagons on the way up to the quarry, as unofficial rubbish in them (old bikes have been reported!) could cause damage at the furnaces. An aside connected with this signal box can be noted here:

About 1952 a man named Butler gave himself up, confessing to having strangled his lady friend in a wood nearby and asking the signalman to telephone the police. The box had no outside phone, and

Wroxton Quarries. Peckett locomotive BASIC takes a train, with brakevan, towards Banbury, 17th June 1965. View taken from the Warwick road bridge.   (M. J. Leah)

Wroxton Quarries. There were few overbridges on ironstone systems, but Oxfordshire Ironstone had three. Shown here is the Southam Road bridge, Banbury, with diesel locomotive ALLAN approaching with a loaded train on 7th August 1967.

(M. J. Leah)

signalman had an uneasy time while the message was relayed to the head office, who contacted the police.

In the mid-1960s a grading plant was installed across the main line from Pinhill Farm shed, on the site of the old kilns. Loaded hopper wagons were taken to an upper level siding so that their loads could be discharged into the grader below and the 'fines' taken away via a low level siding. This practice did not last for very long, however. In 1964 there were plans to install a sintering plant at the cost of about a million pounds, but this was never implemented, as production continued to decline.

The track from Wroxton westwards was double to the Dyke Lane bridge, single through it, then double again as far as the level crossing to Hornton Grounds; and in conformity with operations east of Wroxton, right-hand working was in force. There were two lines at the commencement of the Alkerton branch, but these joined up immediately west of the bridge, where a colour-light signal protected

Wroxton Quarries. Another overbridge, over the road to Horley, with steam locomotive ALLAN bringing up empties to the quarries, with brakevan, April 1964.
(M. J. Leah)

the entrance to the quarry. Also, on the bridge a lookout was stationed, with a wooden hut for protection, as at Balscott Bridge. A cast-iron tank on 'stilts' stood near the Hornton Grounds level crossing, beyond which the track was single, the locomotive propelling the empties in and hauling them out.

At the other end of the system were the sidings of Alcan Industries Ltd,which gained access to BR via the O.I. connection; terms for this right-of-way were agreed in 1930 but it is uncertain when rail traffic commenced—possibly about October 1938 when O.I. sold Alcan half an acre of the 'canal field'. In 1940 Alcan bought a locomotive but before this it is possible that O.I. carried out shunting, as they did from April 1965 onwards, when Alcan sold their diesel locomotive, the work for which had declined.

Wroxton Quarries. ALLAN emerging from under the Warwick road bridge, 7th August 1967. This was the so-called 'German Bridge' as it was built by German prisoners-of-war. When this photograph was taken, single line working was again in force. (M. J. Leah)

The closure and afterwards

The decimation of ironstone quarry systems throughout the East Midlands was a sure pointer to the closure of O.I., but to railway enthusiasts the system was an institution, and closure unthinkable—why, the company had only just purchased a completely new fleet of diesel locomotives! Realities gave a harsher view; O.I. had indeed moved with the times and instituted improvements and economies to keep down the cost of placing the ore on rail. The large size of their operations helped them to do this but when orders began to fall, with overheads remaining very much the same, difficulties were obvious. And fall they did—dramatically. An output of 40,000 tons per week at the end of 1965 dropped by mid-1967 to a mere 2,000 tons per week; and the workforce, which had been 190 at the mid-1950s dropped to about 135 in 1963 and was down to 52, working a two-day week, in 1967. With the reduced locomotive usage, single-line working, on the newer line as far as Drayton Crossisng, was introduced in the Spring of 1967. At this time there were two main line locomotives in use and three at Wroxton, working Hornton Grounds, Alkerton and the crusher; Balscott quarry had closed in October 1966. The quarries were well placed to serve, as they had done, Staffordshire and South Wales, but a long way from either and freight charges on BR continued to rise, whatever efforts were made to cut costs of putting the ore on rail. Thus it came as no surprise when the *Banbury Guardian* of 20th July 1967 carried the news that O.I. would close at the end of September.

Several of the locomotives had already been transferred to other work in Stewarts & Lloyds control, and the others followed in quick succession, leaving *Jean* to provide such movements as were necessary, while the forlorn-looking *Maud* and *Joan* were the sole occupants of the long shed at Wroxton, surrounded by emptiness; but they too soon went. The only other locomotive left was *Sir Thomas*, earmarked for preservation and still treated with loving care by Bill Rogers; she was moved from Pinhill Farm to Wroxton in January 1968, and kept in the workshops behind steel doors and under lock and key—but with the motion greased.

The main contractors employed on the dismantling were Bayons of Cardiff, with Wencas Ltd in a presumed subsidiary capacity. As stated, *Jean* was used as required, and up to the early Spring of 1968 a thread of line was maintained as far as Alkerton, a mixture of right- and left-hand track seemingly chosen at random; the Balscott branch and Hornton extensions had already been lifted and the quarry areas returned to agriculture. The contractors, surprisingly, also introduced a 'locomotive' of their own, and a mighty curious machine it was too. This was a Baguley railcar built in 1940 for the War Department for carrying personnel and had seen service at a number of military establishments, mainly in South Wales; she is thought to have been a 'one off' as far as this country is concerned but she was not used much on O.I. and disappeared as mysteriously as she had come.

There were no locomotives to go for preservation other than *Sir Thomas*, but there was keen competition for the former GWR brakevans, which were quickly snapped up by preservation bodies, as follows:-

1. Keighley & Worth Valley Railway. February 1968.
2. Mr W. H. McAlpine, Hayes. May 1968.
3. Mr D. Alexander, Embsay. January 1968.
4. Great Western Preservations, Didcot. November 1967.
5. Scrapped c April 1968.
6. Severn Valley Railway. September 1967.
7. Scrapped May 1968.
- Southern Locomotive Preservations. February 1968

Some efforts were made to preserve a section of the line along with *Sir Thomas* and one of the locomotive sheds as a permanent example of an ironstone quarrying railway, but nothing came of this, probably because of the scale of operations here. It might have been possible to preserve a section of a small compact system, but at O.I. it would have been necessary to retain quite a lot of track and plant to be representative of ironstone quarrying practice; and it must be remembered that public interest would probably not be very great for a purely industrial railway that few people knew. So the dismantling continued apace; the wagons—dumpcars mostly—were cut up, the quarry machines sold; the last diesel locomotive, *Jean*, left for Glendon 14th May 1968 and the last portion of running track lifted the following day, leaving bits of rail here and there at Wroxton and at Hornton Grounds level crossing. The Hornton quarry face had been pulled over to a 1 in 8 grade and the main area under cultivation, as was Balscott quarry; here the face was landscaped except for the secton nearest the road, where a near-vertical face was planted with trees instead. Digger *D3* was still here in May 1968. There still remained some of the bigger engineering features—the bridge over the Southam road (demolished week ending 20th June 1969), the crushing plant (demolished about the same time), Pinhill Farm locomotive sheds (demolished 1969). The Moor Mill signal box was damaged by fire 23rd April 1968 and was demolished, as was the one at Wroxton. The Wroxton buildings west of the level crossing were left intact and there were a few railside signs and gradient posts, though these soon disappeared, probably into private collections! A surprising survival was the base of the kilns, still visible. During its death throes O.I. became part of the nationalized steel industry and became known as 'British Steel Corporation, Oxfordshire Ironstone Office'. Here Mr Young remained, brooding sadly over the contrast between the bustling activity of a mere ten years before and the present decay. Bill Rogers did not long survive the closure, passing away in December 1969 after a spell in hospital; the loss of everything he had worked for need not have had anything to do with his death—on the other hand, it well might, for he felt it keenly; and who is to tell? Mr Young died at the end of 1980, constantly depressed by the turn of events, but as history showed, the end was inevitable.

The leases were determined as from 31st March 1971 and the former quarrying areas henceforth the concern of the original owners, principally the Oxford colleges; but half a century of intense activity involving the removal of 33 million tons of ore has left plenty of signs, notwithstanding the efficiency of modern restoration methods. At the BR end the 'Ironstone Mines Signal Box' has gone of course, but the site of the sidings is very clear, with the layout obvious almost half way to Cropredy, and at the south end curving away westward parallel to the canal; if you walk along the canal towpath you can look across and note the O.I. embankment and the bridge, still standing, over the farm track—the only underbridge left. Beyond the Southam Road bridge site the trackbed is clear for most of the way through an area that as far as the Warwick road bridge has been used for factory development (Banbury Borough Council purchased this in 1969) and for housing; and much of the route has been adapted for public access.

In 1982 the site of Pinhill locomotive shed was a weedy expanse, and houses were under construction on the hillside overlooking the site; but the latter is still (1984) accessible and even boasts a quarter-mile post—the 1¼ milepost with the figures missing. The old cutting, overgrown but recognisable still, leads off uphill and on the left is the concrete-faced bank that led to the kiln tops; the route continues as before, with rock cuttings here and there, all the way to the Banbury-Warwick road. Housing estates now cover much of this area and the trackbed has been utilized for pedestrian access; one section runs eastward from a suburban road ('Highlands') that has replaced a footpath that once crossed the line, and a crude tunnel runs under the concrete filling carrying the road over the trackbed.

Wroxton Quarries. View from the bridge to the former Alkerton Quarry, showing the trackbed revealed by crop marks. 2nd August 1975.
(Eric Tonks)

A little further west we come to a cul-de-sac named 'Ironstones' and from here to the Warwick road bridge the route is tarmaced, with a tunnel under the new concrete Warwick road bridge that crosses the site on a straight alignment. There are other roads on the estate bearing names having associations with iron—eg. 'Ferriston', 'Hearthway'. Beyond the Warwick Road the first quarter mile has been filled to ground level and incorporated in playing fields, but the route can be picked up at Drayton Crossing and from here to Moor Mill level crossing the trackbed is clear as a designated footpath; an interesting

Wroxton Quarries. The long locomotive shed at Wroxton, 2nd August 1975. Note the two sections, the older at the rear; also conifer plantations on old workings.

(Eric Tonks)

exhibit just west of Drayton on the south side is a ruined brick and concrete blockhouse, a relic of World War II. The level crossing gates at Moor Mill have been replaced by wire fencing, the signal box has gone, and a short section of the trackbed used as access to an official car park; just beyond here the trackbed is blocked but can be picked up again beyond the site of the Horley bridge and followed all the way to Wroxton; this, probably the most scenic part of the route, winding first through a wide and shallow cutting, then between a rock face and the plantation on Friars Hill, and finally on a ledge of the hillside, was acquired in November 1982 on a 21-year lease from Trinity College as a Nature Reserve by the Berkshire, Buckinghamshire and Oxfordshire Naturalists Trust[1]. This happy outcome—mainly due to the perseverance of Tony Nash—for the 65-year-old site, prevented its being turned into a motor-cycle track.

Only the concrete base of the crusher is to be seen on the bank overlooking the main trackbed, but beyond the level crossing site all the major buildings remain except for the signal box. Wroxton yard and office block have been used by a succession of small companies; J. O. Wright & Co Ltd, a firm of structural engineers, used the long locomotive shed and yard, while the office block was occupied first by Farm Animal Equipment Co Ltd, and from 1976 by J. J. Thomas (Farm Tractor Sales) Ltd, both using the address 'Old Ironstone Works, Wroxton'. In 1984 Clarke Storage & Haulage Ltd and associated companies took over the site with the address quoted as 'Ironstone Works, Wroxton St Mary'. These successive owners have made few changes to the site, that apart from the missing railway tracks looks much as it did in O.I. days; but the workshops retain track and inspection pit and the locomotive sheds still have their 'pots'—and in the case of the long shed, track also.

Beyond Wroxton the trackbed and quarry areas have mostly been restored to agriculture, but the lower level of the excavated fields is very obvious from the Stratford road, where the fine bridges to Balscott and Alkerton quarries have been left unaltered for farm access. An area north of the long locomotive shed and west of the trackbed has been planted with larch and pines. The terminal faces of the Balscott Pit have been smoothed over and grassed except for the sections nearest the road, where the steeper slopes have been planted with larch, spruce and beech. Likewise the near-vertical rockwall alongside the road by the New Inn has been left and is overgrown with ash trees and shrubs. Look over the fields from the Alkerton bridge alongside; the

Wroxton Quarries. Cutting between Friars Hill and Horley—now a Nature Reserve.
9th October 1982.   (Eric Tonks)

trackbed site is revealed in differences in the colour or height of the crop. 'Wroxton Heath Bridge' on Dyke Lane is also in place, but further north the road from Hornton towards Wroxton is not elevated above the fields, as it was excavated at the same time. The restored areas are crossed by replacement hedges—hawthorn in many cases (eg. across Balscott pit), wire in others. An 'island' of hard rock remains in the old Langley Quarry site.

Hornton quarries have been fully restored to agriculture but the water tank remains by the road. Just beyond the former ironstone quarry is a small quarry owned by Hornton Quarries Ltd, which up to 1982 was the home of an ex-O.I. machine, still in its maroon livery and bearing traces of its number, *D1*. This did not appear then to be used and by 1984 it had gone. Other ex-O.I. machines exist still (1981) at Alkerton quarries in the ownership of Peter Bennie Ltd, who took over in 1969, using lorry transport. The stone is sold for various purposes—large for building, small for roadmaking, fine as filler. For a period some was even used for ironmaking; this was sent to Banbury station and loaded into rail wagons by a mechanical grab for despatch to Bilston or Shelton ironworks, at the rate of about 500 tons per day;

this traffic ceased on 16th June 1978, but a few loads were later sent to Llanwern.

Bennie has considerably extended the Alkerton workings, well beyond the O.I.limits; some of his earlier pits have been filled under the guise of 'Oxfordshire County Council Alkerton Quarry Waste Disposal Site'—yet the former O.I. quarry site remained unfilled and with wire fences crossing it, with a 'high wall' between it and the Bennie site (1981). But it hardly brings much pleasure to those who knew the quarries as a working unit, and the industrial enthusiast will find more satisfaction in exploring the substantial remains of the railway system.

Footnote

1. *Banbury Focus*, 25th November 1982; thanks to John Betts for this information.

Grid References

462429	Junction with GWR
459426	Bridge over road to Hardwick Farm
455428	Bridge over Southam road
449421	Main locomotive sheds and workshops/kilns
447420	Bridge under Warwick road
432420	Drayton crossing
421431	Moor Mill level crossing
418433	Horley lane bridge
410430	Friars Hill crusher
407428	Wroxton level crossing
407427	Old locomotive shed for quarries, with workshops
405427	New locomotive shed for quarries
406427	Offices
393428	Langley Quarry
403431	Dyke Lane bridge
382439	Hornton branch level crossing
380450	Hornton quarry terminus
400421	Bridge to Balscott quarries
386434	Bridge to Alkerton quarries

Steam Locomotives

Gauge; 4ft. 8½in.

No.1 SIR THOMAS	0-6-0T	OC HC	1334	1918	16 x 24in.	3ft. 9in.	New 4/1918	(1)
		Reb	HC	1955				
No.2 LORD NORTH	0-6-0T	OC HC	1346	1918	16 x 24in.	3ft. 9in.	New 10/1918	(2)
No.6 FRODSHAM	0-6-0ST	IC MW	1013	1887	12 x 17in.	3ft. 1⅜in.	(a)	(3)
No.8 GOWY	0-6-0ST	IC MW	1119	1889	12 x 17in.	3ft. 1⅜in.	(a)	(3)
No.14	0-6-0ST	IC MW	1749	1909	12 x 17in.	3ft. 0in.	(b)	Scr 1/1938
NANCY	0-6-0ST	IC HE	356	1885	13 x 18in.	3ft. 1in.	(b)	Scr 6/1926
IRONSTONE	0-4-0ST	OC HE	344	1885	13 x 18in.	3ft. 1in.	(c)	(4)
No.3 THE PRESIDENT	0-6-0T	OC HC	1419	1923	16 x 24in.	3ft. 9in.	New 7/1923	(5)
NOEL	0-4-0ST	OC P	1172	1912	14 x 20in.	3ft. 2in.	(d)	(6)
PHYLLIS	0-4-0ST	OC WB	1453	1895	13½ x 20in.	3ft. 6in.	(e)	(7)
No.4 THE DEAN	0-6-0ST	IC HE	1496	1926	16 x 22in.	3ft. 9in.	New 7/1926	(8)
No.5 TREASURER	0-6-0ST	IC HE	1446	1929	15 x 22in.	3ft. 7in.	New 7/1929	(9)
No.5 BASIC	0-6-0ST	OC P	1867	1935	16 x 24in.	3ft. 10in.	New 6/1935	(5)
No.6 GWEN	0-4-0ST	OC HC	1662	1936	14 x 22in.	3ft. 3½in.	New 4/1936	(8)
GRACE	0-4-0ST	OC P	1894	1936	14 x 22in.	3ft. 2½in.	New 9/1936	(10)
MAUD	0-4-0ST	OC P	1937	1938	14 x 22in.	3ft. 2½in.	New 1/1938	(10)
SIR CHARLES	0-6-0ST	OC P	1943	1938	16 x 24in.	3ft. 10in.	New 2/1938	(5)
THE BURSAR	0-6-0ST	OC HE	1645	1930	14 x 20in.	3ft. 4in.	(f)	(8)
		Reb	HE	1940				
JOHN (JOAN to 8/1957)	0-6-0ST	OC P	1981	1940	14 x 22in.	3ft. 7in.	New 12/1940	(10)
ALLAN	0-6-0ST	OC P	1997	1941	16 x 24in.	3ft. 10in.	New 7/1941	(5)
SPENCER	0-6-0ST	IC HE	2374	1941	16 x 22in.	3ft. 9in.	New 8/1941	(5)
GRAHAM (HELLIDON to 4/1953)	0-6-0ST	IC HE	2415	1941	18 x 26in.	4ft. 0½in.	(g)	(5)
BYFIELD No.2	0-6-0ST	OC WB	2655	1942	15 x 22in.	3ft. 4½in.	(h)	(11)
MARY	0-4-0ST	OC HC	1818	1950	14 x 22in.	3ft. 3½in.	New 8/1950	(10)
NEWLAY	0-4-0ST	OC HE	1292	1917	15 x 20in.	3ft. 4in.	(i)	(12)
BARNSLEY	0-4-0ST	OC HC	727	1905	14 x 20in.	3ft. 3½in.	(j)	(13)
ALEX	0-6-0ST	IC HE	3716	1952	16 x 22in.	3ft. 9in.	New 2/1952	(10)
BARABEL	0-4-0ST	OC HC	1868	1953	14 x 22in.	3ft. 3½in.	New 7/1953	(10)
BETTY	0-4-0ST	OC HC	1869	1953	14 x 22in.	3ft. 3½in.	New 7/1953	(10)
PHYLLIS	4wVBT	VCG S	9615	1956	6¾ x 9in.	2ft. 6in.	New 7/1956	(10)
303. No.2. JOAN	0-4-0ST	OC AE	1822	1919	14 x 20in.	3ft. 3in.	(k)	(10)
JEAN (BETTY to 5/1958)	0-4-0ST	OC HC	1696	1939	14 x 20in.	3ft. 3½in.	(l)	(10)
FRANK	0-6-0ST	IC HE	3872	1958	16 x 22in.	3ft. 9in.	New 11/1958	(5)

(a) ex Topham Jones & Railton Ltd, hire 4/1919.
(b) ex Ministry of Munitions, Gretna, 5/1919.
(c) ex Lloyds Ironstone Co Ltd, Corby, 4/1923.
(d) ex Baldwins Ltd, Netherton, Staffordshire, 6/1924.
(e) ex Alfred Hickman Ltd, Bilston, Staffordshire 2/1965.
(f) ex Hunslet Engine Co Ltd 11/1946; orig. Haifa Harbour Works, Palestine.
(g) ex Park Gate Iron & Steel Co Ltd, Charwelton Quarries, 1/1943.
(h) ex Byfield Ironstone Co Ltd, Byfield Quarries 9/1944.
(i) ex Steel Co of Wales Ltd, Margam, 5/1951.
(j) ex HC, loan, 1/1952.
(k) ex Steel Co of Wales Ltd, Margam 1/1957.
(l) ex E. L. Pitt & Co (Coventry) Ltd, Brackley, Northamptonshire 1/1958. Prev. Royal Arsenal, Woolwich.

(1) to London Railway Preservation Society, Quainton Road station, 6/1969.
(2) Scr on site by James Friswell & Son Ltd 6/1958.
(3) returned to Topham Jones & Railton Ltd.
(4) to Stewarts & Lloyds Ltd, Corby 1/1933.
(5) Scr on site by Friswell 9-10/1955.
(6) to Horsley Bridge & Thomas Piggott Ltd, Great Bridge, Staffordshire 8/1946, then to Stewarts & Lloyds Ltd, Bilston 12/1946.
(7) Scr on site by Friswell 3/1956.
(8) Scr on site by Friswell c.5/1969.
(9) to Stewarts & Lloyds Ltd, Corby 1/1933.
(10) to G. Cohen Sons & Co Ltd, Cransley, for scrap 9/1965.
(11) to Loddington Ironstone Co Ltd, 1/1947.
(12) Scr on site by E. L. Pitt & Co (Coventry) Ltd 4/1964.
(13) returned to HC 8/1953.

Diesel Locomotives

Gauge; 4ft. 8½in.

GRACE	0-4-0DH	S 10090	1961	311hp	30 tons	New 12/1961	(1)
MAUD	0-4-0DH	S 10142	1962	311hp	30 tons	New 12/1962	(2)
JOAN	0-4-0DH	S 10165	1964	311hp	30 tons	New 9/1964	(3)
GWEN	0-4-0DH	RR 10200	1964	311hp	30 tons	New 10/1964	(4)
BETTY	0-4-0DH	RR 10201	1964	311hp	30 tons	New 12/1964	(4)
BARABEL	0-4-0DH	RR 10202	1964	311hp	30 tons	New 12/1964	(5)
MARY	0-4-0DH	RR 10203	1964	311hp	30 tons	New 12/1964	(6)
JEAN	0-4-0DH	RR 10204	1965	311hp	30 tons	New 1/1965	(7)
ALEX	0-4-0DH	RR 10205	1965	311hp	40 tons	New 6/1965	(1)
JOHN	0-4-0DH	RR 10206	1965	311hp	40 tons	New 6/1965	(1)
GRAHAM	0-4-0DH	RR 10207	1965	311hp	40 tons	New 7/1965	(8)
ALLAN	0-4-0DH	RR 10208	1965	311hp	40 tons	New 7/1965	(1)
FRANK	0-4-0DH	RR 10209	1965	311hp	40 tons	New 7/1965	(9)

(1) to Stewarts & Lloyds Ltd, Corby Steelworks 10/1967.
(2) to Stewarts & Lloyds Minerals Ltd, Market Overton Quarries 2/1968.
(3) to S&LM, Harlaxton Quarries 3/1968.
(4) to S&LM, Harlaxton Quarries 9/1967.
(5) to Stewarts & Lloyds Ltd, Bromford Tube Works, Birmingham, 7/1967.
(6) to S&LM, Woolsthorpe Quarries 9/1967.
(7) to S&LM, Glendon East Quarries 5/1968.
(8) to Stanton & Staveley Ltd, Stanton Ironworks, Derbyshire, 8/1967.
(9) to S&LM, Market Overton Quarries 10/1967.

Quarry Machines

Fleet	Model	Type	Maker/Serial	Year	Capacity	Reach	New	Ref
	103c	S. Shovel	Bu				New 1918	(1)
	X 92	S. Shovel	Marion 3770	1918	4 Cu.Yds.	30ft.	New 5/1918	(2)
No.9	12 ton	S. Navvy	Wilson 111				(a)	(3)
No.22		S. Crane	Wilson 305				(a)	(3)
No.8		S. Navvy	RP 403	1914	1½ Cu.Yds.	25ft.	(b)	(4)
		S. Crane	NBM			35ft.	(c)	(5)
	C type	S. Navvy	Wh		3½ Cu.Yds.		(d)	(6)
JIMMY	No.20	S. Navvy	RP				(e)	(7)
	No.20	S. Navvy	RH 573	1920			New 1/1920	(8)
SYD (No.1 to 1935)								
	No.20	S. Navvy	RP 429	1915			(f)	(9)
	X 92	S. Shovel	Marion 5956	1930	4 Cu.Yds.	30ft.	New 5/1930	(10)
	480	S. Dragline	R&R 237	1935	1¾ Cu.Yds.	65ft.	New 3/1935 (g)	(11)
	480	S. Dragline	R&R 511	1937	2 Cu.Yds.		New 6/1937 (h)	(11)
	422	D. Dragline	R&R 673	1937			New 8/1937	(12)
	490	E. Shovel	R&R 1015	1939			New 12/1939 Scr c. 1956 (i)	
E 1	100RB	E. Shovel	RB 5896	1941	3½ Cu.Yds.	32ft.	New 8/1941	(13)
D 3 (D 4 to 7/1956)								
	43RB	D. Dragline	RB 6995	1942			New 11/1942	(14)
WINSTON 2	54RB	D. Dragline	RB 6997	1943	2½ Cu.Yds.	26ft.	New 4/1943(j)	(15)
W 1 (B 1 to 9/1956, WINSTON to 1/1956)								
	54RB	D. Shovel	RB 8647	1948	2½ Cu.Yds.		New 2/1948	(16)
E 2	100RB	E. Shovel	RB 12374	1951	3½ Cu.Yds.		New 2/1951	(17)
D 2 (D 3 to 7/1956)								
	43RB	D. Dragline	RB 14060	1951	1 Cu.Yd.	70ft.	New 7/1951	(18)
D 1	43RB	D. Dragline	RB 15952	1953	1 Cu.Yd.	70ft.	New 8/1953	(19)
B 3 (WINSTON 3 to 1/1957)								
	54RB	D. Shovel	RB 15578	1953	2½ Cu.Yds.		New 11/1953	(20)
B 4	71B	D. Shovel	BE 115698	1956	3 Cu.Yds.		New 3/1956	(21)

(a) ex Topham Jones & Railton Ltd, Contractors, hire 4/1919.
(b) ex Frank Edmunds, dealer, 5/1919.
(c) ex Inland Waterways Docks & Engineering, Richborough, Kent 8/1919. Rebuilt as diesel with 40ft. boom, by Smith, Rodley, Leeds, No. X 59975.
(d) ex ?, 9/1919. Chain Bucket.
(e) ex ?
(f) ex Alfred Hickman Ltd, Sydenham Quarries c.1926.
(g) Shovel from 3/1944.
(h) Fitted with shovel end.
(i) Fitted with dragline gear.
(j) Shovel from 5/1957—2½ Cu.Yds. 26ft.

(1) to James Friswell & Son Ltd, Banbury, for scrap 10/1949.
(2) s/s c.1952.
(3) returned to Topham Jones & Railton Ltd.
(4) to Friswell for scrap 3/1939.
(5) to Peter Court, dealer, Balscott, c.1967.
(6) engine and boiler to crushing plant 10/1936.
(7) s/s c.1946.
(8) s/s c.1944.
(9) s/s c.1942.
(10) s/s c.1953.
(11) Scr by Friswell as from 9/1955.
(12) to ?. Cardiff 3/1945.
(13) Balscott Qy. To ?, Scotland 1/1968.
(14) to ?. c.7/1968.
(15) to R. Wright, Staffordshire Public Works Dept. 8/1968.
(16) Alkerton Qy. To ?. 12/1967.
(17) Alkerton Qy. To Peter Bennie Ltd 10/1967.
(18) Balscott Qy. To Peter Bennie Ltd 3/1968.
(19) to Hornton Quarries Ltd 5/1967.
(20) Balscott Qy. To Peter Bennie Ltd 11/1967.
(21) to ?. 7/1967.

The Warwickshire Quarries

EDGE HILL QUARRIES

Owners: Edge Hill Light Railway Co.

The ironstone quarries at Edge Hill were small and shortlived, of little consequence to the ironmaking industry, and for interest, were completely eclipsed by the unique transport system, the Edge Hill Light Railway. To us, visiting it in the 1930s, the attraction lay in its status as a statutory Light Railway and the sombre spectacle of its decaying relics and its sad history, so ably related in the *Railway Magazine* for April 1931 by J. G. Aston, J. R. Hollick and D. S. Barrie. That it served an ironstone quarry was obvious; that this was a curious circumstance in itself was not. But it served as a stepping-stone to investigate nearby Oxfordshire Ironstone, and then other ironstone systems; indeed, but for the EHLR this book might not have been written.

Promotion of the Light Railway

As noted under the Wroxton heading, during World War I the Home Ore Department of the Ministry of Munitions was anxious to develop the North Oxfordshire orefield, and the first steps to implement these wishes seem to have been early in 1917 on the initiative of the Earl of Dudley, who owned land in the vicinity of Edge Hill. It was estimated that there were 30 million tons of ore available in the neighbourhood, and it was proposed to start working this at the escarpment outcrop. The nearest railway line was the Stratford-on-Avon & Midland Junction Railway, a struggling system eager to promote any possibility of mineral traffic, of which iron ore was the most important; they must have been approached by Lord Dudley or by his Agent, G. C. Bond, and it was through the SMJ that the scheme came to public notice. Harry Willmott, Chairman of the SMJ, was interviewed by a representative of the *Birmingham Gazette* and his comments published also in the *Banbury Guardian* of 28th March 1917. He stated that the ore lay within three miles of the SMJ and that it was proposed to build a line from Kineton; however, the article refers also to the 'ariel' (sic) trolley line at Burton Dassett, so probably this was even then regarded as the most likely junction. It was hoped that the Government would be prepared to provide a subsidy of £20,000 to finance the work, and a further suggestion was that the quarries be worked by German prisoners-of-war. Another account(*Banbury Guardian*, 5th April 1917) gave the thickness of the orebed as ten feet under only two or three feet of overburden. The major drawback to this proposal was the rope-worked incline required to negotiate the steep Edge Hill escarpment.

Samples of ore were submitted (probably by George Bond) to the Ministry of Munitions, who pronounced them to be of good quality, self-fluxing and not requiring calcining; at the same time, they considered the proposed transport method too costly (letter from G. Percy Stanley in *Banbury Guardian* 26th April 1917). This decision would almost certainly have been influenced by the Ministry's commitment to the alternative scheme for opening up the orefield by an outlet to the GWR near Banbury and which led to the formation of Oxfordshire Ironstone Co Ltd. Baldwins Ltd were the prime movers in the latter scheme and their mining engineer, Alex Mackay, had an interview with George Bond 'early in 1917', as recorded by Frederick Scopes in his *The Development of Corby Works*; he suggested a pooling of their interests, using the Banbury outlet as preferable to the Edge Hill incline. Mr Bond however was not convinced, doubtless mindful that the Earl of Dudley's properties were close to the escarpment, considerably further from Banbury than Baldwin's leases; and efforts were continued to make the connection with the SMJ.

On 26th April 1917 the chairman, deputy chairman and engineer of the SMJ visited the Edge Hill site to 'prospect for the proposed branch railway' (*SMJ Board Minutes*, 16th May 1917). At this time another Black Country company, T. & I. Bradley & Sons Ltd, with furnaces at Darlaston, had acquired mineral leases over 600 acres of ground in the parishes of Warmington, Ratley and Horley, and they entered into negotiations with the other interested parties over the matter of transport. Financial assistance from the government not being forthcoming, and the quarry owners seemingly unwilling or unable to find the capital for building the line, the unique step (as far as the ironstone industry is concerned) was taken to promote a separate company under the Light Railways Acts of 1896 and 1912. Public notice of this appeared in August 1917 (*Banbury Guardian*, 23rd and 30th August 1917) in the form of a notice headed 'Edge Hill District Mineral Light Railway Order 1917', the promoters being William James

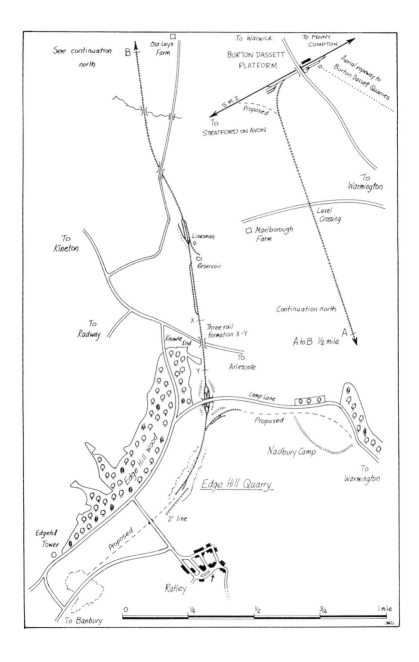

Foster, Herbert Spencer Thomas and Harlod Jeans, who were directors of T. & I. Bradley & Sons Ltd of Darlaston and of the associated company T. & I. Bradley of Bilston; the object was stated to be 'to authorise the incorporation of a company under the above title'.

Powers were sought for a standard gauge line 11¼ miles in length, mostly in Warwickshire, but extending over the boundary into Oxfordshire. Under this scheme the main line ran practically straight from the SMJ at Burton Dassett Platform to Edge Hill, which it ascended by a cable-worked incline a quarter of a mile in length, then along the top of the hill roughly south-south-west as far as Sunrising Hill and beyond that, south to Rough Hill Farm, midway between the villages of Epwell and Shenington; and there were two branches, one running from Knowle End (at the head of the incline) eastwards towards Warmington, parallel to Camp Lane, and a longer one to Horley Fields, leaving the main line just beyond the Round Tower; and a reverse curve at Burton Dassett Junction for traffic running in the Stratford direction. For Parliamentary purposes the various sections of line were referred to by numbers; the main line comprised railways 1, 3 and 4 (No. 1 from the SMJ to the road crossing just short of the foot of the incline, No. 3 thence to just beyond the summit, and No. 4 to the terminus); railway No. 2 was the reverse curve, while the Camp Lane and Horley branches made up railways 6 and 5 respectively.

The mineral leases were almost wholly disposed along railways 4, 5 and 6 on the plateau. Railway 6 served T. &. I. Bradley's ground alongside Camp Lane, in Warmington parish, railway 5 tapped their Horley leases, while railway 4 passed through their Ratley lease southwest of the village. The area between Camp Lane and the Ratley lane (about 157 acres) was owned by the Earl of Dudley, who also owned the escarpment area of about 800 acres, for almost a mile both north and south of Sunrising Hill; all this would be served by railway No. 4, while the extremity of the latter in the vicinity of Shenington ran through an area leased by G. C. Bond on his own account, and possibly other persons. The Earl of Dudley's properties were administered by The Edgehill Co Ltd, a company registered in September 1917 with the Earl as principal shareholder. The title Edgehill Ironstone Co has appeared in print, possibly one used by G. C. Bond in respect of his properties, or an error for Edgehill Co Ltd; it is impossible to be certain from the context. As will be seen, the situation was a complex one, and the guiding principle in constructing the EHLR was to open up Bradley's lease by Camp Lane first, followed by those of the Earl of

Dudley, then the others. However, before anything could be done, it was necessary to obtain approval for the light railway—in contrast to the normal ironstone approach of obtaining a wayleave from the landowners and local authorities.

The project attracted a good deal of attention, both friendly and hostile, locally and the Light Railway Commissioners, under the chairmanship of Mr A. E. Gaythorne Hardy, held a Public Inquiry in Banbury Town Hall on the 8th and 16th November 1917. The light railway promoters were supported by the SMJ and owners of mineral rights to be worked; opponents included the occupiers of Upton House and Upland Farm, who contended that the railway would interfere with the residential and agricultural amenities of their estates; and some local authorities whose chief objection was the level crossings, of which there were fourteen, mostly on minor roads. It may also be mentioned that the termini of the branches were at altitudes lower than the junctions, the Camp Lane branch having a gradient of 1 in 50 for some hundreds of yards.

After a tedious legal battle, modified proposals for the railway were agreed upon, whereby the main line would terminate at Sunrising House, the branch to Horley Fields abandoned, and the Camp Lane branch shortened—leaving a total of 5¾ miles, all in Warwickshire; the company also agreed to tunnel beneath roads on the upper section. The commissioners also insisted that, should the project prove successful, the decisions to grant the order should not prejudice any further attempts to extend the railway.

The engineer of the railway was H. F. (later Colonel) Stephens, the wellknown light railway champion; and at the inquiry he revealed that originally it had been planned to make the junction at Fenny Compton, where the line would have had access both to the GWR and SMJ; but this was abandoned in favour of the shorter route. Like the light railway, the title was also shortened to 'Edge Hill Light Railway'. The inclusion of the incline caused protracted negotiations in the matter of rates, it being finally agreed to permit the EHLR to charge a royalty on all goods conveyed over the incline; and on 17th July 1918 an Order was submitted to the Board of Trade, who affixed their seal on 20th January 1919.

The authorized capital was £90,000 and the line was to consist of three sections; a low level portion (over which the SMJ were to have running powers, and passengers could be carried), 2 miles 5 furlongs 3½ chains in length; an incline of 2 furlongs 6¼ chains; and a high level section of 2 miles 5 furlongs 8 chains. A speed limit of 12 miles per hour was imposed and a maximum load of 12 tons per wheel. Following the authorization of the EHLR, Bradley's transferred their ironstone properties to the Banbury Ironstone Co Ltd, formed in March 1919 from the interests of Bradley & Foster Ltd (successors to T. & I. Bradley Ltd), Shelton Iron & Steel Co Ltd, and The Blaenavon Co Ltd; the new company administered the leases at Warmington and Ratley—the Horley leases being abandoned. The EHLR became a subsidiary of Banbury Ironstone Co Ltd.

Layout and Equipment

Construction began early in 1919 and in all some 3¼ route miles of track were laid. The EHLR left the SMJ just west of Burton Dassett Platform, where the accommodation comprised two reception sidings, a weighbridge and turntable, and the approach of the light railway was protected by a signal of SMJ pattern and a runaway siding; from here the line curved away sharply and ran almost due south, with a slightly descending gradient from each end, to the foot of the hills, where it crossed a lane by a girder bridge and broke into a series of reception sidings in a shallow cutting. At the southeastern end ran a spur to a concrete-lined reservoir that supplied water for locomotives through a pipeline by gravity.

The incline had a ruling gradient of 1 in 6, eased off at each end, raising the railway from 400 to 700 feet above sea level; a little less than half way up, it crossed the gated lane to Arlescote by a girder bridge, adjoining which the company built a number of wooden bungalows. The rail formation was unusual, the lowest portion being single, the middle portion double track, and the section upwards from the bridge of three-rail formation with the centre rail common to both tracks; this last economises in rail and earthwork without the necessity for points as would be required by reduction to single track. At the summit these rails converged to one track, then divided into three, the flanking two at a slightly higher level; this section was in cutting. A linesman's hut at the foot was in telephonic communication with a similar building at the top of the incline. The latter was operated by the usual funicular principle of descending full wagons hauling up the empties; the steel cable ran on rollers between the rails up the incline and at the summit beneath the rails and round a horizontal wheel about 15ft. in diameter, supported in a pit just south of the Camp Lane

Edge Hill Quarries. Railway incline viewed from the storage sidings, 28th May 1935. Locomotive No. 1 on left. The double track portion and the bridge over the Arlescote lane can be seen. (H. C. Casserley)

Edge Hill Quarries. The inclined bridge over the gated lane at Arlescote, May 1947. E.H.L.R. notice on left, near hutments. (Eric Tonks)

bridge. The braking was controlled from a hut on the north side of the bridge. Camp Lane bridge was of substantial girder construction spanning three tracks, and displayed warning notices against trespass, with the SMJ lettering erased and replaced by 'Edge Hill Light Railway' in white paint. Beyond the bridge the line curved southwestward, with a trailing junction to the Nadbury Branch, and then entered the quarrying area.

The railway was equipped almost completely from secondhand sources, a feature common enough among light railways but not usual for ironstone quarry lines, again emphasising the unusual character of this system. The track, for instance, was anything but uniform; spiked on the low level section and on the incline, chaired in the reception sidings and at points, and an indiscriminate mixture of both on the high level. Point levers were of the adjustable self-reversing type. There were no signals apart from the one at Burton Dassett Junction, the line being worked on the 'one engine in steam' principle, for which purpose the low and high level sections were offically regarded as two railways.

The locomotives on the low level section were undoubtedly the star attraction to railway enthusiasts, being two of the famous London, Brighton & South Coast Railway 'Terriers' that were so well suited for light railway work. *No. 1* came from the Longmoor Military Railway (it having been requisitioned for war service) in May 1919 and *No. 2* from the LBSCR in July 1920; these dates were supplied by Mr C. R. Hughes, Secretary of the EHLR, and presumably refer to the dates of arrival, the dates July 1919 and June 1920 quoted elsewhere probably referring to the date of sale by the former owners. A special point of interest is that *No. 2* was of class A1 and *No. 1* of class A1X, having been rebuilt with modified boiler and extended smokebox in 1912. Both were painted in the earlier Southern Railway livery of green lined black edged white and lettered E.H.L.R. in white on the tank sides, and the numbers on the bunker sides.

Subsequently *No. 1* was relettered in the odd style E.H.L.T.R., with the letters equally spaced but separated by stops and with the T smaller than the other letters. There was no shed for these engines; water was available from the reservoir, coal probably at Burton Dassett. Washing-out, repairs etc were carried out at Stratford (SMJ) shed where the 'spare' locomotive was kept as a rule; at other times the locomotives stood in the open, covered by tarpaulins, at Edge Hill. Also on the low level were two ex-Great Eastern Railway brake vans purchased from the War Department and numbered 1 and 2. The

'Terriers' were used on constructional work.

When the upper section was opened, a third locomotive was obtained in June 1922 to work it; this was a small Manning Wardle saddle tank with no dome, a neat chimney and a small weatherboard only for the protection of the driver. She was a typical contractor's design, had a couple of large sandboxes and, between the pairs of buffers, further pairs of wooden blocks for shunting narrow gauge wagons when operating on mixed track. Named *Sankey*, she had worked on the Manchester Ship Canal in the ownership of Topham, Jones & Railton. It is curious that the same firm had been building the Oxfordshire Ironstone railway in the period 1919-22, but this appears to have been no more than coincidence. *Sankey* had a livery of dark red, lined black edged yellow, but with traces of an earlier green livery; the nameplates were of brass. She ascended the incline under her own steam, assisted by cable haulage, with two wagons as counterweight (Mr S. C. Button in the *Railway Magazine* June 1936, p.451). Like the two 'Terriers', she had no shed but utilised the shelter of the Camp Lane bridge, plus a tarpaulin. Water was obtained from a tank wagon that stood on the siding next to the engine and was replenished from the reservoir as required and coal from a heap thrown down by the lineside. There was a workshop and forge-cum-office in a field adjoining. For digging the ironstone there was a Ruston & Proctor steam navvy, said to have come from Richard Thomas & Co Ltd at Port Talbot, and carrying the stencilled number 3022; she had two pairs of wheels on each axle, of gauges 4ft. 8½ins. and 7ft. 3ins. Rolling stock owned by the railway consisted of some 60 wooden side-tipping wagons of 'Ship Canal' type, some coming from the Manchester Ship Canal contract, and some from the SMJ; they were used on constructional work, but iron ore would presumably be despatched in wagons supplied by the various ironworks.

The Quarries in Production

Construction of the railway was a long-drawn-out affair and it was not until the summer of 1922 that the incline was completed and the line extended to the quarrying area, production commencing later in the same year, under difficult economic conditions. The siding agreement with the SMJ was dated 1st March 1922. The policy seems to have been to combine the tasks of railway construction and ore production. The boundary fences of the 'main line' of the light railway were installed as far as the lane to Ratley, and also for the Nadbury branch as far as Camp Lane. The branch lay almost entirely within the Banbury Ironstone Co lease, hence the start of construction of this at the earliest possible moment, so that the owners of the EHLR could develop their own leases in accordance with their original intentions. As things turned out, the Nadbury branch never extended more than a few yards, and the whole of the ironstone excavated came from the main railway cutting. A gullet was driven along the southeast boundary fence, and track laid down; overburden from the ground ahead was conveyed in side-tipping wagons running on 2ft. gauge 'Decauville' track to the standard gauge railhead, tipped into the wooden side-tipping wagons and used to build the embankment of the Nadbury branch.

Dr J. R. Hollick, examining the site in 1930, thought that the ironstone excavated by the steam shovel was also loaded into 'Ship Canal' wagons that were taken by *Sankey* to the elevated outer sidings at the incline head and the contents shovelled into main-line wagons standing on the lower central line; these were then taken down the incline and despatched to ironworks in the Black Country and North Staffordshire. As the ironstone face moved further away from the main track, a point was installed and temporary track laid along the face. Under these conditions of working, progress in constructing the light railway was dependent on the demand for ironstone, which in the early 1920s could only be described as fitful. As the face reached the boundary fence, the railhead was pushed forward; but it never got further than about halfway between Camp Lane and the Ratley lane. A couple of shallow pits were started just beyond the end of track, the route otherwise undisturbed; but at the Ratley lane there was an extraordinary exhibit in the form of a 'bridge' for double track, with brickwork and parapets, but only partially cleared out beneath, the space occupied by a few rails and some concrete fence posts with various stamped dates in 1919 and 1920. Beyond the bridge the route was pegged out for a few hundred yards but not excavated.

It seems certain that all the ore despatched by the EHLR came from its own cuttings, which was logical inasmuch as it was in the promoters' interest to work their own property first, and the Order stipulated a five-year limit for the construction of the railway. The despatch tallies give the consignor as the Edge Hill Light Railway Co, which was therefore performing purely as an ironstone operator in its own right, yet having legal standing very different from that of Oxfordshire

Ironstone Co Ltd, which was owned jointly by the lessees of the properties it served. The annual returns to the Minister of Transport describe the EHLR as a 'railway under construction' with 'lines not open to traffic', with the cost of the line increasing from year to year, even when the railway lay dormant; there are no indications that the railway was ever open for traffic in the form of revenue or operating expenses, from which it seems that the rolling stock was regarded as part of the equipment required for constructional purposes and was charged as such; and that receipts and payments were respectively deducted from or added to the cost of the line; this information was supplied by Mr A.L.F. Fuller in his letter of 3rd September 1946. The light railway promoters used the line as an ordinary tramway during the construction period and the leases alongside the railway were never opened up.

From the operational point of view the interest of the light railway lay in the incline, the only standard gauge example in the industry, but it did not see much use, nor was it entirely free from trouble. On one occasion *Sankey* nearly followed its train, giving the driver an uncomfortable time, but fortunately nothing more serious than a derailment resulted. A fatality did occur, however, in 1924, when a

Edge Hill Quarries. Track on the Arlescote Bridge, 2nd June 1942, showing cable, rollers, etc. The railway had by then been disused for 17 years. (Rev. A. V. W. Mace)

runaway on the incline took place whilst the chairman, Mr Harry Willmott, was paying a visit of inspection; Mr Ferguson, the engineer was accompanying him and pulled him clear, but was knocked down himself and died of his injuries; the wagons plunged on and crashed into one of the 'Terriers'. When in production about 35 wagons per day were sent down the incline; known customers were Bradley & Foster, Darlaston: Midland Coke Coal & Iron Co Ltd, Apedale; R. S. Hingley & Sons, Netherton; but there were probably others in Staffordshire. Because of the precarious state of the iron industry, production was intermittent and there were several temporary closures.

Among the few visitors to the railway was the celebrated railway historian, C. R. Clinker, who was 'born almost within sight of the railway' and was taken there on numerous picnicking occasions by his father, who also kept a diary—and information extracted from these has been used in this account; Clinker Sr. also took about 30 'first class quarter plate photographs' of the railway in action, including some of wagons on the incline and one of *Sankey* at an angle of 45° near the terminus as a result of rail subsidence. These unrepeatable views were all lost in the World War II 'Blitz' on Bristol that destroyed his photograph collection; it is ironic that Mars, the god of war that brought the EHLR into being should be the instrument of destruction of the best (and probably only) photographic record of the working railway. It was the younger Clinker's regret, no doubt, having been given this rare opportunity of seeing a railway under construction, that it should turn out to be such an unfortunate venture; but the vivid experience remained with him always, as childhood memories do. He recalls that working sometime took place on a Saturday or Sunday—'why, we never knew'. The only other known visitor in this period was G. W. Carter, who came in April 1923 and gave his observations in a letter dated 22nd August 1947: a 'Terrier' was at the foot of the incline, the other not seen (probably being at Stratford) and the excavation of the cutting was about 50 yards south of Camp Lane bridge.

Activity Suspended

The closure of the railway is imperfectly remembered locally, with conflicting accounts probably arising from the several temporary holdups in production. D. S. Barrie (one of the authors of the *Railway Magazine* article) tells us that the last load of ore was despatched from

Edge Hill Quarries. Track at top of incline, 11th May 1930. Hut for controller on left. Note stop-blocks on centre line, rollers etc. (Dr J. R. Hollick)

Burton Dassett on 27th January 1925, according to the book of the yard foreman, implying closure of the quarry on that or the previous day. The caretaker of later years, Mrs. Moore, had records of men being paid up to 1927, and kindly showed these to us; but for what purpose these men were paid was not stated. Clinker made several visits in 1925–26 and saw no trace of activity, and 'grass had started to appear at the mines'. He went on: 'it was these last visits that really bore in upon me the tragedy and waste of the whole sorry business'.

Aside, it can be mentioned that in 1925 Oxfordshire Ironstone were having a very thin time, and Edge Hill very unlikely to have been in a better position; so for all practical purposes we feel that the 27th January 1925 date must be accepted. Anent this, Clinker said in his letter of 27th September 1946: 'there is an amusing story behind the confirmation of the date 27th January 1925 being obtained from the Burton Dassett yard book; when we meet I will try to recount it to you'. Unfortunately we never did meet in the privacy required for the exchange of confidences, so there the matter rests; but Clinker is usually regarded as rather an austere man who took railway history very seriously, and these nostalgic letters reveal the gentler, more instrospective and lighter side to his nature.

As the months lengthened into years and chances of a resumption of work faded, on a normal ironstone system the railway would have been lifted and the equipment sold; but as a statutory railway, the EHLR owned the land on which it was laid and required legislation for abandonment, so it was left in a kind of 'Sleeping Beauty' situation of frozen immobility, waiting for the kiss of life. Even after 20 years of dereliction, the sorry remains contrived to give an air of suspended activity. The 'Terriers', brakevans and some 40 wagons were collected in the sidings at the foot of the incline; at the top was *Sankey* under Camp Lane bridge, with its water tank alongside. About 20 wagons were disposed along the cutting or by the start of the Nadbury branch,

Edge Hill Quarries. Looking down the cutting to the lower sidings from near the summit, May 1937.   (H. G. Tonks)

Edge Hill Quarries. Incline, near the summit, May 1949. Earth slips have covered the trackbed. (B.G.S.)

the Ruston navvy at the end of the cutting, and a few narrow gauge tip-trucks. The locomotives were protected by tarpaulins and up to 1940 there was a caretaker living in a wooden bungalow by the Arlescote lane bridge. For seventeen years their isolation was undisturbed except by occasional railway enthusiasts and chance visitors, the latter no doubt surprised to see such incongruous dereliction in the green countryside. The locomotives lost their plates (a maker's plate off *Sankey* was auctioned at Sotheby's many years later) and small fitments, and brakevan No. 1 was manoeuvred on to the 'main line', where it ran away and came to rest at the lowest point, halfway to Burton Dassett Junction. Nature and the elements took their toll of the rolling stock, ill-protected as it was, and of the permanent way, particularly on the incline, where falls of earth at the summit buried the rails and, lower down, left them in mid-air; while brambles, saplings, a profusion of wild flowers and remains of cable made the ascent a difficult matter for the walker. In 1938 the Southern Railway considered purchasing the 'Terriers' as a source of spares for their

Edge Hill Quarries. The Camp Lane bridge, viewed from the quarry area, May 1947. (Eric Tonks)

surviving locomotives of the same class (as they purchased the Shropshire & Montgomeryshire Railway *Daphne*) but the advanced decay of the engines and the difficulty of moving them caused the idea to be abandoned.

Requisitioning of the Light Railway

The outbreak of World War II brought hopes of a resumption of work, just as World War I had led to the opening of the quarries; but in this case the rail connection was already in existence—in poor shape, admittedly but, with fresh locomotives, capable of being restored to working order. Representations were made to the Ministry of Supply for government help in this direction; but the Home Ore Department of the Ministry of Supply, like the Ministry of Munitions of World War I, declined, taking the view that the national interest would better be served by increasing production at Oxfordshire Ironstone[1]. Hard on the heels of this decision (and very probably a factor in it) came the construction of what became known as C.A.D. Kineton, but which started off as the 'Marlborough Farm Munitions Depot' (Marlborough Farm adjoined the EHLR half a mile from the junction).

Edge Hill Quarries. Interest at Edge Hill centres almost exclusively on the Light Railway; but some quarrying for ore did take place, even if only in laying the railway line. This view, looking towards the end of the track in May 1947, shows the ironstone face. Note the different types of track. (Eric Tonks)

The depot covered a large area of the Warwickshire plain at the foot of the hills, including the site of the Battle of Edge Hill, and its railway system was connected with the LMSR at Burton Dassett. Almost the whole of the EHLR main line, from Burton Dassett Junction, to a point about 100 yards north of the reception sidings at Edge Hill was requisitioned on 2nd October 1941 and a further furlong 19th March 1943, by the War Department. Construction of this project had begun in October 1940 on ground adjoining the EHLR; track in the requisitioned area was lifted and practically all traces effaced by the extensive sidings of the new depot, radiating from a junction close to the site of the EHLR junction; a new signal box of modern design replaced the ground frame formerly used. The weighbridge and turntable belonging to the light railway had been demolished some years before by the LMSR in the mistaken belief that they were LMSR property.

Brakevan No. 1 was taken over by the WD and used by them, being broken up in 1946[2]. The WD locomotive depot was at the junction.

Edge Hill Quarries. 'Terrier' No. 1 in the lower sidings. This locomotive was the rebuilt class A 1X. Photographed Summer 1945. (J. E. Norris)

The underbridge at the northern end of the Edge Hill reception sidings was officially requisitioned and the girders removed but in fact the boundary fence of the depot fell short of this point. Some of the rails in the sidings and on the lower part of the incline were removed, apparently because it was erroneously thought that they were WD property, and the company therefore erected suitable notices at the boundary of the still privately-owned portion. Thus it came about that the most interesting part of the EHLR—the incline, locomotives, and most of the rolling stock—escaped immediate extinction, and many locomotive enthusiasts were glad of the opportunity of seeing the relics. Not that they were a happy sight; the winds had whisked away the last tattered shreds of tarpaulin and the 'Terriers', more easily identifiable in their declining years by the LBSC lettering beneath the eroded EHLR paint, were red with rust; as one saddened 'Brighton' fan chalked on a tank—'O Tempora! O Mores! that a Stroudley Terrier should come to this'.

Edge Hill Quarries. 'Terrier' No. 2 in the lower sidings. This locomotive was in the original form, Class A 1. (Collection Eric Tonks)

Edge Hill Quarries. Manning Wardle locomotive SANKEY, under the Camp Lane bridge, June 1941. (L. W. Perkins)

Edge Hill Quarries. Water tank standing next to SANKEY, 14th June 1946; this was the only water supply available, water being brought up the incline from the reservoir at the foot.   (O. H. Prosser)

Hopes for Revival of Quarrying

Removal of the low level section effectively ruled out the EHLR as a means of transporting ironstone to the BR network, but there were still hopes of reopening the quarries, no less than three attempts being made to do so. All three, in some form or other, referred to the light railway, which was also the subject of protracted legal discussion; these affairs and the abortive efforts to reopen the quarries ensured that the area was continually in the local press for a further 20 years. On 19th October 1944 the Sheepbridge Co Ltd purchased from Corpus Christi College, Cambridge, an area of 600 acres in the parishes of Ratley & Upton and Epwell; part of the former Upton Estate, this had been bought by the college 23rd October 1936 from the executors of Mr A. R. Motion. The college was aware of its potential value as a source of ironstone but kept it purely as agricultural land; the estate indeed had refused a competing offer from 'one of the leading iron and steel companies'[3]. Shortly after purchase, Oxfordshire Ironstone obtained permission to bore trial holes. The Sheepbridge purchase complemented to the south and east the area held by Edgehill Co Ltd

Edge Hill Quarries. Derelict wagons at the start of the Nadbury branch. Nadbury Camp is in front of the trees in the background, on the far side of Camp Lane. Summer 1945. (J. E. Norris)

Edge Hill Quarries. Vera Tonks peering beneath the uncompleted bridge under the lane to Ratley, May 1947. The parapets were complete but only minor excavation beneath. View from the south side. (Eric Tonks)

225

and Banbury Ironstone Co Ltd adjacent to the EHLR, so could have been served by any revival of the light railway. Nothing came of this and that very year, 1944, it was decided to sell the rolling stock for scrap; but negotiations involving the transfer of the deal to the Ministry of Supply caused delay, and it was not until the Spring of 1946 that the demolition contractor, James Friswell & Son Ltd of Banbury, brought his equipment to Edge Hill; he cut up the low-level stock first and then dealt with the upper section, finishing the job in August. The last member to go was the navvy, whose jib, projecting above the surrounding fields, had been a familiar sight from the road for 21 years; a close inspection would have revealed some half-charred potatoes in the firehole left by a picnic party of Oxford undergraduates when they lit a fire in the old machine, and were surprised by the caretaker.

In 1947 Staveley Coal & Iron Co Ltd acquired control of Bradley & Foster Ltd, the associated company Banbury Ironstone Co Ltd and its subsidiary Edge Hill Light Railway Co. The remaining isolated track was useless for getting away any ore in the event of reopening of the quarries, and the EHLR company sought compensation accordingly—failing reinstatement of the requisitioned portion —from the WD; whilst the latter claimed that, as the railway had been derelict for many years when they acquired the site, the company were only entitled to the price of the land and scrap value of the equipment, and they offered this amount when serving a Notice to Treat for Compulsory Purchase, dated 14th June 1949. Litigation contined for several years, culminating in a hearing before the Lands Tribunal in London in January 1956, at which the author's booklet on the railway[4] was quoted on both sides as the only unbiassed account available. The Lands Tribunal gave judgement, in the report of 21st February 1956[5], in favour of the WD, ie. upholding the latter's contention that the EHLR were only entitled to the price of the land and scrap value of the equipment, basing their decision on the fact that the company had never taken any steps to resuscitate the line until the possibility of some compensatory money arose, and that propositions made since that time were always made on the assumption that full compensation would be paid.

The formal end of the EHLR came about at a meeting in Birmingham on 25th November 1957, when the company went into voluntary liquidation; Mr C. R. Hughes (Secretary both of the light railway and of Banbury Ironstone Co Ltd) was appointed liquidator, with instructions to dispose of the land and remaining assets. The remaining

Edge Hill Quarries. Ruston steam digger at the end of the track, May 1937. The jib. protruding over the top of the quarry face, could be seen from the road along the Edge Hill escarpment, on the far left.

(H. G. Tonks)

track was removed April to September 1957 by James Simms (Leamington) Ltd.

While the fate of the EHLR was in the melting pot, efforts to resume quarrying at Edge Hill continued unabated, with Sheepbridge in the fore. The *Birmingham Mail* of 8th February 1952 reported an application received by the Minister of Housing to work 'a very considerable deposit of ironstone at Edge Hill' in the parish of Ratley & Upton, and in view of the 'special visual amenities' of the area, the county planning authority was proposing a Public Inquiry. This took place on 22nd and 29th July 1954 at the Municipal Buildings, Banbury, at which the Sheepbridge Co Ltd and Banbury Ironstone Co Ltd made a joint application to work ironstone over 735 acres in the parishes of Ratley & Upton, Shotteswell and Warmington; this includes the 600 acres purchased by Sheepbridge in 1944 plus the adjoining land owned by Edgehill Co Ltd and Banbury Ironstone Co Ltd. Mr C. R. Hughes (Secretary of Banbury Ironstone and of the EHLR) spoke of the possibility of reopening the latter, subject to a favourable outcome of the negotiations with the WD. An output of 200,000 tons per year over 25 years was envisaged. The application was opposed by landowners, the Birmingham Archaeological Society and the Council for the Preservation of Rural England. Much of the discussion centred on the historic Iron Age earthen fort known as Nadbury Camp, which was included in the proposed quarrying site; though not scheduled as an Ancient Monument by the Ministry of Works, the latter had asked that it be excluded from the permitted quarrying area. It was however suggested at the inquiry that a suitable compromise could be arrived at whereby both archaeology and ironstone operators could benefit by careful excavation. It was also stated that the quarrying would not affect the local industry in Hornton Stone (for building purposes) that lay beneath the pure ironstone bed[6]. Warwickshire County Council were indifferent to the effects on the scenery and were quite happy, provided the ore was to be removed by rail and not over the inadequate roads of the district.

The finding of the Public Inquiry, issued in 1956, was that permission to mine in the area would be granted, even Nadbury Camp, provided that care was taken to preserve any relics of antiquarian interest and that the original contours of the Camp would be restored when the ore was removed. By then the fate of the EHLR had been sealed, but plans for reopening the quarries were still being considered. The Sheepbridge holding was leased to Oxfordshire Ironstone for 60 years from 1st July 1959 but Uplands Farm and Manor Farm were sold to farmers, subject to the rights of Oxfordshire Ironstone to extract the ironstone under the terms of the lease, which however was never exercised[7]. Then the *Banbury Guardian* of 21st November 1963 reported that Sheepbridge was "to cut in a big area near its present mining site at Ratley", implying that quarrying was already in progress—which was not the case, nor was any further quarrying for iron ore ever done. Indeed, the areas where excavation had been done by the EHLR were disposed of. James Simms (who had lifted the track in 1957) and Arthur Tickle applied to use the cutting as a refuse tip but this was strongly opposed by local residents and their objection endorsed at a Public Inquiry[8]. The whole of the area ever used by the EHLR (other than that requisitioned by the WD of course) was sold to a Mr Spratt of Coventry in October 1966.

Present-day Remains

Considering the short working life of the Edge Hill quarries, the evidence of them on the ground is quite substantial, and yet another facet of the unique character of its transport system, the EHLR. The status of the latter precluded immediate dismantlement and return of the ground to agriculture, as with nearly all ironstone quarry tramways; and since all the ironstone quarried came from railway land, the line was left undisturbed until the company was wound up. The only major change since then has been the dismantlement of the remaining bridges in the late 1960s; Arlescote Lane bridge was demolished and the banks suitably graded, Camp Lane and the Ratley lane filled in beneath and the parapets razed to ground level and grassed over, marked now only by replacing fences. As for the forces of Nature, well, they had been active for 40 years already and the process merely continued, with much of the ground becoming ever more heavily overgrown; the trees in the summit cutting were 30ft. high by 1980.

A public footpath crosses the lower sidings site, and to the north the embankment toward the dismantled bridge remains, littered with rotting sleepers and a few anonymous chairs, and heavily overgrown of course and an inspection is only really possible in winter; beyond this the army depot has engulfed all traces of the low level main line. On the south side of the footpath the area once covered by railway lines is well defined but has been used for shooting and other purposes and there is not much to be seen.   The same applies to the lower part of the incline. On the upper side of the Arlescote Lane bridge site is a wooden hut, presumably of railway origin, and the start of the railway cutting here towards the summit is very clear, though overgrown, and can be followed all the way to the blocked-off Camp Lane bridge; in the early 1980s the undergrowth was impassable but is now (1984) traversable. There was a proposal to fill this in but happily this seems to have been abandoned. Even some of the original features can be seen; a section of the wall where the flanking sidings were at a higher level than the main line, and the brickwork of the cabin at the top of the incline.

The quarry area offers the best preserved remains, with well-marked rock faces each side. This too had been let for shooting for a time and a few conifers planted for cover, near the road. The Nadbury branch site has however completely gone, absorbed into the fields. Beyond the end of the gullet, Nature in a rough mood takes over again and it is wisest to return to the road; but the whole scene is highly evocative—and to those who knew the EHLR in its declining days, very nostalgic.

Footnotes

1. Frederick Scopes, *The Development of Corby Works*, p.269.
2. T. Walker, *The Railway Observer*, June 1948, p.113.
3. Upton Estate files, Corpus Christi College.
4. *The Edge Hill Light Railway*; the story of an unfortunate line. Eric S. Tonks, 1948.
5. *Estates Gazette*, 17th March 1956, CLXVII, p.252.
6. *Banbury Guardian*, 29th July 1954.
7. BSC Archives.
8.*Banbury Guardian*, 25th February 1965.

Grid References

378524	Junction with SMJR
381495	Bridge over road to Northend
382487	Bridge over lane to Arlescote
382483	Bridge under Camp Lane
380477	Bridge under Ratley lane
381478	End of quarry
385486	End of Nadbury branch

Locomotives

Gauge; 4ft. 8½in.

1		0-6-0T	IC B t o n		1872	12 x 20in.	4ft. 1in.		(a)	(1)
			Reb Bton 1912							
2		0-6-0T	IC B t o n		1872	13 x 20in.	4ft. 0in.		(b)	(2)
SANKEY		0-4-0ST	OC MW 1088		1888	10 x 16in.	2ft. 9in.		(c)	(3)

(a) ex Longmoor Military Railway, 5/1919; formerly LB&SCR 673.
(b) ex London Brighton & South Coast Railway, 674, 7/1920.
(c) ex Topham Jones & Railton Ltd, contractors 1922.

(1) Scr on site by James Friswell & Son Ltd 4/1946.
(2) Scr on site by Friswell 5/1946.
(3) Scr on site by Friswell 6/1946.

Dates of purchase of the 0-6-0T are those quoted by the Edge Hill Light Railway Co, and differ slightly from the LBSCR version.

Quarry Machines

3022	S. Navvy		RP	or	RH		(a) Scr 1947

(a) ex Richard Thomas & Co Ltd, Port Talbot.

BURTON DASSETT QUARRIES

Owners: The Burton Hill Iron Ore Co; Burton Dassett Iron Stone Co from 1895; Willingsworth Iron Co Ltd from 1907; T. &. I Bradley & Sons Ltd from 1918.

The small quarry system at Burton Dassett, though the last in this book, can in no way be dismissed as least; certainly not by us, who have for it a special affection as the very first we saw, in the late 1920s—though it was deserted then. The author and his brother enjoyed many rides on the derelict wagons down the rough track in the shadow of the windmill. But the appeal of Burton Dassett is not purely sentimental, as anyone who has been there will know; for it is a delightful spot with wide views over the Warwickshire 'felden', which has led to its designation as a Country Park. This in turn has ensured the preservation of the quarry site much as it was at its final abandonment, allowing us to study that which it epitomizes and which has practically disappered elsewhere (Easton on the Hill excluded)—the small ironstone quarry of the mid-nineteenth century. One can still imagine without much difficulty how it appeared when at work; and there are enough 'unknowns' in its fragmented history to give anyone the opportunity of adding to our knowledge by enquiry or observation.

The hilltop site imposed two limitations—the area of workable stone was small, and it was isolated from rail transport; but it is easily-won outcrop stone, which was probably what prompted its early exploitation. The quarry escapes all mention in MS, but E. A. Walford, on page 13 of his essay *The Lias Ironstone of North Oxfordshire (around Banbury)* published as a Geological Survey Memoir in 1899, quotes 1868 as the start of operations, when the output would probably be conveyed by horse and cart to the nearest station, Fenny Compton, on the GWR main line. The East & West Junction Railway line from Fenny Compton to Kineton was opened in 1871, and from Kineton to Stratford in 1873, and about this period an aerial ropeway was constructed between the quarries and Burton Dassett goods yard adjoining the Banbury-Warwick road. It seems likely that the goods yard was christened Burton Dassett because of its initial association with the quarries, since the yard is in fact much nearer to the village of Northend, which is (and was then) of greater importance than Burton Dassett, as the latter has practically ceased to exist as a village.

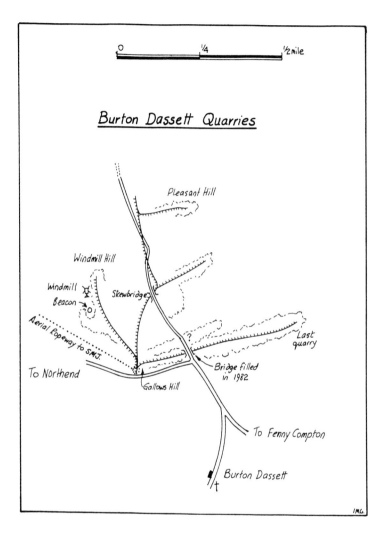

The ropeway was of light construction, with short pylons and small round buckets, haulage being supplied by a portable steam engine at the lower end, according to Mr J. Lloyd of Fenny Compton. Whether a tramway was used in the quarry to bring the ore to the head of the ropeway is unknown, but it seems very likely as it was the usual practice then. Walford gives the quarry as working until 1873 and does not give the name of the operator; but the ledgers of the Birmingham

Railway Wagon & Carriage Co Ltd record that the company (then the Birmingham Wagon Co Ltd) hired railway wagons for the period January 1871 to January 1876 to The Burton Hill Iron Ore Co, the proprietors of which are given as Richard Robbins of Kenilworth and Harold Smith of Grazeley, near Wolverhampton. It is possible that Samuel Lloyd took a hand in working this system, as he refers to the acquisition of the only ironstone working connected with the East & West Junction Railway, 'near Stratford', in his *Reminiscences*, published privately in Birmingham in 1913. This little volume of random recollections is interesting to read but weak on dates — even possibly on chronology—but in this case there is no other known quarry that fits; this would be the middle 1870s.

The ropeway does not appear on the 1885 OS, though the quarries are shown, so had presumably been dismantled by then. The next reference to the quarries appears in *Kelly's Directory* of Warwickshire for 1895 in the form 'The quarries, which have not been worked for some years, are now (1895) about to be opened and a railroad laid down connecting the site with the East & West Midland Junction Railway'. The promoters were Attenborough & Timms, who owned ironstone quarries at Brixworth and Finedon in Northamptonshire and elsewhere, but here operated under the style of Burton Dassett Iron Stone Co. *Kelly's Directory* for 1900 states "The quarries, which had not been worked for some years, were reopened in November 1898 by the Burton Dassett Iron Stone Co and a railroad has been laid down connecting them with the E. & W.M.J.R.". The phrase 'railroad' was presumably copied from the 1895 entry, at which time it was perhaps intended to lay a tramway with a rope-worked incline down the hillside through Northend village, and then overland to Burton Dassett goods yard. Instead, however, another aerial ropeway was installed, by Wm. Glover & Sons Ltd of Warwick, of more substantial construction than the earlier one; it had higher pylons and larger buckets with rectangular tops and triangular section, holding a sixth of a ton. At the lower end the buckets were run off the cable on to a stationary support over a stage, tipped by hand and pushed back on the cable, a secondhand stationary boiler from a ship providing the traction. At the upper end the rope ran round 'the big wheel', where the buckets were loaded with ore brought over a narrow gauge tramway; very probably there was a platform and chute alongside the wheel, as obtained in later years.

On the tramway ponies were normally used for haulage, assisted by

Burton Dassett Quarries. Group of quarrymen about 1895. Extreme right of front row is believed to be Jim Lloyd, who later became caretaker during the dereliction period.   (The Rev. Fermor, Vicar of Northend)

gravity on some stretches. We say 'normally' because for a short time a steam locomotive was tried out. The make and origin of this locomotive is unknown, but its existence is vouched for by Mr R. W. Hunt, uncle of Mr A. R. James, whom we met at Cadeby Rectory in April 1967. Mr Hunt, then in his eighties, said that he had lost his parents when a boy and had been brought up in Northend by his grandmother until she died in 1904; then, after being 'pushed from pillar to post', he joined the Royal Warwickshire Regiment in 1909. The locomotive was here during this period (1898-1909); asked to describe it, he likened her to *Pixie*, the Bagnall locomotive belonging to the Rev. E. R. Boston at Cadeby (and of course a former ironstone locomotive). Obviously he chose a locomotive with which he was familiar, corresponding broadly to the one at Burton Dassett. Without pushing the analogy any further, it is just possible that she was one of the first two Bagnalls at Finedon quarries, sent here for trial purposes. Finedon quarries were operated by the Barlow family, but the quarry leases were held by Attenborough & Timms. There is, however, nothing to substantiate this theory, in Bagnall's records of spares, for example; Messrs A. C. Baker and R. T. Russell have searched their files on this subject. It was not on site long, as the experiment was not much of a success, mainly because there was no readily available supply of water, which had to be carted up the hill from the village. However, Mr Hunt remembers her "pulling wooden tubs up to the big wheel" and we must leave this minor but intriguing facet of the Burton Dassett quarries there, hoping that someday perhaps identification will be possible.

The working life of the quarries was again only short; LQ lists them as operating in 1899 (corresponding with the opening in November 1898), 1900 and 1901 during which time the total workforce dwindled from 53 to 15. For the period 1902-1906 the quarries are described as 'standing', for the first three years under the ownership of Attenborough & Timms and for the last owned by J. H. Yates, whoever he was. For 1907-1909 ownership is credited to Willingsworth Iron Co, thus bringing Burton Dassett into the ambit of the Staffordshire ironmasters, as were most of the Oxfordshire quarries; but only for 1908 are any figures given for the 'number of men employed', and in this case only seventeen, so there could not have been much done. In 1908 quarrymen at Pleasant Hill, north of the Beacon, came across a Saxon burial chamber with 35 skeletons. An SMJ board minute of 29th June 1909 records that 'An Agreement has been completed with the Willingsworth Iron Co to lease land, buildings and plant on our land' formerly leased to Attenborough & Co; but Willingsworth did no more. The last annual report to H.M. Inspector of Mines & Quarries was dated 23rd January 1908 and on 1st January 1912 he was informed that 'the mines had been abandoned'. This information comes from the company ledgers preserved by their successors, Patent Shaft & Axletree Co Ltd; thanks are due to Mr Bailey for extracting them. *Kelly's Directory* for 1912 records "No active operations have been carried on since 1909". Incidentally, *Kelly's* continued to quote the owners as Burton Dassett Iron Stone Co for 1908-1910, but whether the title was continued under Willingsworth tenure is uncertain—and it hardly matters!

The increased demand for iron ore in World War I brought about a further and final reopening of Burton Dassett quarries, this time by T.& I. Bradley & Sons Ltd, who were also the promoters of the Edge Hill Light Railway. The SMJ board minutes of 14th February 1916 record: "T.& I. Bradley have acquired 200 acres at Burton Dassett and propose to extract ironstone and use sidings temporarily at an early date with the existing overland plant and then later to extend the sidings and put down calciners". In fact reopening for production did not take place until 1918, in which year the stationary engine was reconditioned by Bell Bros of Stratford. The layout at the quarries, as noted well after the final closure, consisted of three lines radiating from the 'big wheel' on the western face of Gallows Hill, with subsidiary branches to the working faces; the track was of two foot gauge and wagons were the familiar V-shaped side-tippers, that ran on to a platform at the lower end so that their contents could be tipped into the buckets via a chute,. In later days there was only a very small workforce and only one pony to move the wagons both up and down. Hand labour (hard labour, too...) was the rule, though there was some blasting of harder stone. Output was a mere 100 tons per day. Two of the lines passed beneath the unfenced lane to Northend by wooden bridges.

The system was inherited from Willingsworth's 1908 operations, as a letter in the *Banbury Guardian* of 12th April 1917 under the nom-de-plume 'Verb. Sap. Sapiente' states that all plant—wagons, sidings and the track at the then idle quarries—were still available for re-use. The date of the closure is uncertain; Mr J. Lloyd, who had been responsible for the stationary engine, gives it as 1921, when he was kept on as caretaker, his duties including that of running the mechanism from time to time. Another version, in *The Geology of the Country Round Banbury and Edge Hill* published by HMSO in 1965, states that the 'overhead tramway was in use during 1925 but working ceased a short time after'. It has been said that the closure was at the request of the landowner, who refused to allow the contours of the hills to be altered further; but so many quarries succumbed in the postwar economic depression that they would have been closed anyway—and the retention of the caretaker is at variance with this tale, which probably referred to Windmill Hill only.

Much of the information in this account, other than where the source is specified, comes from Mr Lloyd's recollections, which included some on a lighter note. The ropeway was sometimes used as a means of passenger transport between the SMJ and the pits—a long way round by road—but occasionally things went wrong. Once, the lunch whistle blew with a traveller aboard and the engineman, conscious only of the demands of the inner man, stopped the cable; fortunately, the man was only a couple of pylons away from the summit, which he managed to reach hand-over-hand. He fared better than another luckless man, who was only halfway when a thunderstorm broke over the Burton Hills, of such violence as to cause the cessation of work and with it the ropeway; marooned 50ft. above ground in a swaying bucket that rapidly filled with water, and without a vestige of shelter from the driving rain, the rider had no choice but to sit it out; these trips being entirely unauthorised, he had no redress, but doubtless did not make another for some time!

After a few years it became apparent that there was little likelihood of reopening and about 1929 the system was abandoned, and dismantled a few years later—by James Friswell & Son Ltd of Banbury, it is believed. The ropeway disappeared, including the bridge over the road to Northend, the tramway tracks taken up and the wagons removed; but the quarry site was otherwise unaltered apart from filling in of the bridge. It might be mentioned that the site has much historical interest, with its stone beacon tower and the old windmill; the latter was restored in 1931 and preserved by order of Lord Willoughby de Broke, the landowner, but was struck by lightning during a violent storm on 26th July 1946; the body toppled into the ironstone quarry

Burton Dassett Quarries. Burton Dassett Hills, showing the quarry face around Beacon Hill and tramway cuttings to other workings. These lines converged to the top of the cableway at bottom left, just off the picture. (Collection Mrs B. Gulliver)

Burton Dassett Quarries. Beacon Tower and Post Mill. The quarry face beneath the beacon is clearly shown.

(Oxfordshire County Libraries)

Burton Dassett Quarries. View in the Country Park, 6th September 1975. The old quarry tunnel was reopened by the Country Park authorities, but was soon filled in again because of pressure of traffic on the road. (Eric Tonks)

alongside, the damage being so severe as to preclude rebuilding. This historic interest, coupled with the scenic attractions of the site, led to its designation as the Burton Hills Country Park on 3rd September 1972, which has ensured the preservation of the quarried area, rightly regarded as part of the history of the site. Better than that; one of the former tunnels that had been filled in was knocked through again, with a new concrete roof to support the road, and the former trackbed made into a 'trail'. Unfortunately, the volume of traffic using the Park was such that subsidence of the road occurred, and the tunnel was filled in again in 1982. The site of the wheel can easily be identified, and the tramway routes to the various working faces made out; the last working face, at the extreme southeastern corner, is the best defined. A very pleasureable way to spend an hour or so, and a worthwhile objective for a walk through some of Warwickshire's nicest countryside—and with the chance of learning something fresh. Of the ropeway there are no certain traces; there is no sign of where it crossed the lane to Northend, but in the rough field on the west side of the latter are two groups of stones that might be the remains of pylon bases.

Grid References

379526	Ropeway loading terminal
389522	Ropeway crossing of road to Northend
396520	Bridge over quarry line
395521	Beacon quarry
397520	Last quarry

Locomotive

Gauge; 2ft. 0in.

0-4-0ST	OC	WB (?)	(a)	s/s

(a) ex ?

EXPLANATION OF TABLES

Locomotives

The columns show in order:- title: type:cylinder position: maker: maker's number: year built: cylinder dimensions: driving wheel diameter: origin: disposal. In referring to these columns the following points should be noted.

Title. Unofficial names used by the staff but not carried by the engine are denoted by inverted commas.

Type. The Whyte system of wheel classification is used, but if wheels are not connected by outside rods they are shown as 4w, 6w as the case may be. The following abbreviations are used:

T	Side Tank	DM	Diesel Mechanical	BE	Battery Electric
PT	Pannier Tank	DE	Diesel Electric	WE	Wire Electric
ST	Saddle Tank	DH	Diesel Hydraulic		
WT	Well Tank	PM	Petrol Mechanical		
VB	Vertical Boiler	PE	Petrol Electric		
G	Geared	PMR	Petrol Mechanical Railcar		

Cylinder Position

IC	Inside Cylinders
OC	Outside Cylinders
VC	Vertical Cylinders

Makers. The following abbreviations are used, with lesser known builders' names being given in full.

AB	Andrew Barclay Sons & Co Ltd, Kilmarnock.
AE	Avonside Engine Co Ltd, Bristol
AP	Aveling & Porter Ltd, Rochester
B	Barclays & Co, Kilmarnock
BEV	British Electric Vehicles Ltd, Southport
Bg	E. E. Baguley Ltd, Burton on Trent
BH	Black Hawthorn & Co Ltd, Gateshead
Bton	Brighton Locomotive Works, LB&SCR
CF	Chapman & Furneaux Ltd, Gateshead
DC	Drewry Car Co Ltd, London (Suppliers only)
DK	Dick, Kerr & Co Ltd, Preston
EE	English Electric Co Ltd, Preston
EV	Ebbw Vale Steel Coal & Iron Co Ltd, Ebbw Vale
FE	Falcon Engine & Car Works Ltd, Loughborugh
FH	F. C. Hibberd & Co Ltd, London
FW	Fox Walker & Co, Bristol
GB	Greenwood & Batley Ltd, Leeds

GEC/USA	General Electric Co, USA
H	James & Frederick Howard Ltd, Bedford
HC	Hudswell Clarke & Co Ltd, Leeds
HCR	Hudswell Clarke & Rodgers, Leeds
HE	Hunslet Engine Co Ltd, Leeds
HL	Hawthorn Leslie & Co Ltd, Newcastle upon Tyne
Hu	Robert Hudson Ltd, Leeds
JF	John Fowler & Co (Leeds) Ltd
K	Kitson & Co Ltd, Leeds
KE	Kilmarnock Engineering Co Ltd
KS	Kerr, Stuart & Co Ltd, Stoke on Trent
Mkm	Markham & Co Ltd, Chesterfield
MR	Motor Rail Ltd, Bedford
MW	Manning Wardle & Co Ltd, Leeds
N	Neilson & Co, Glasgow
OK	Orenstein & Koppel AG, Berlin
P	Peckett & Sons Ltd, Bristol
RH	Ruston & Hornsby Ltd, Lincoln
RR	Rolls Royce Ltd, Shrewsbury
RS	Robert Stephenson & Co Ltd, Newcastle upon Tyne and Darlington
RSH	Robert Stephenson & Hawthorns Ltd, Newcastle upon Tyne
S	Sentinel (Shrewsbury) Ltd
Sdn	Swindon Locomotive Works, GWR
SS	Sharp Stewart & Co Ltd, Glasgow
VF	Vulcan Foundry Ltd, Newton-le-Willows
WB	W. G. Bagnall Ltd, Stafford
YE	Yorkshire Engine Co Ltd, Sheffield

Maker's Number. Reb = Rebuilt.

Year Built. The year quoted is that given on the maker's plate, or from the maker's records if the date does not appear on the plate.

Cylinder and Driving Wheel Dimensions. These apply to locomotive as new.

Origin. 'New' indicates that the locomotive was delivered by the makers to this location at the stated date (to the month where known). Transfers from elsewhere are indicated by a bracketed letter and appropriate footnote.

Disposal. Locomotives transferred to another owner or site are shown by a bracketed number with corresponding footnote. Scr = Scrapped. s/s = scrapped or sold, disposal unknown.

Explanation of Tables

Quarry Machines

The information is set out in much the same way as for locomotives, but as collected information on quarry machines has not appeared before we give rather more in the way of explanation. The columns show in order:- title (if any): class description: power source and type of machine: maker: maker's number: year built: bucket capacity: jib or boom length: origin: disposal.

Title. Often machines carried no title, but major operators such as Stewarts & Lloyds Minerals Ltd gave them numbers, quoted where known; and a very few were named.

Class Description. Steam machines were most commonly referred to as '10-ton', '20-ton', etc, the 'ton' referring not to the weight but to the cutting pressure on the bucket teeth. Ruston Proctor & Co Ltd adopted these as class numbers, a No. 20 machine being a '20-ton' and so on, and these class numbers have been used in the tables, as in the manufacturer's literature. Whitaker's used a letter code but unfortunately only in a few cases do we know these, so we have had to fall back on '12 ton' etc. Ruston & Hornsby Ltd used designatory numbers for larger machines, e.g. No. 250.

Diesel and electric machines were given class numbers by Ruston Bucyrus Ltd from a scheme used by the Bucyrus Co. The early machines were described as 37B, 43B etc but this was later changed to 37RB and 43RB etc, and we have used the latter throughout for simplicity. The numbers correspond roughly with the weight of the machine in tons. Ransomes & Rapier Ltd applied class numbers such as 422, 480 etc, and also used these numbers for steam machines of the same power. The large Walking Draglines of both manufacturers incorporated 'W' in the class description — 3W, 5W for RB in ascending order of size, and W 150, W 1400 etc for R&R, the numbers again corresponding roughly to the weights.

Power Source and Type of Machine. The power source is indicated by a letter:- S—Steam: D—Diesel: DE—Diesel Electric: E—Electric: PP—Petrol-paraffin.

The two main types of machine are shovels and draglines. In simple terms, the latter were used primarily for removing overburden by dragging the bucket up the working face by a chain in a scraping motion, then slewing the bucket round to dump the load on the worked-out area; a shovel would then dig out the ore beneath. Obviously there are many variants on these according to circumstances, and digger drivers were very adept in using their machines in difficult positions. Some removal of overburden was done by 'stripping shovels' of large size. The form and duties of various specialized machines will be obvious from their names — crane, clamshell, back-acter, etc. Some machines were rail-mounted, some on crawlers or 'Caterpillar' tracks. When the type of machine is uncertain, the term 'navvy' is used.

Makers. The following abbreviations are used, with lesser known builder's names being given in full.

At	Atlantic Equipment Co, USA
BE	Bucyrus-Erie Co, USA
Berry	Henry Berry & Co Ltd, Leeds
Bu	Bucyrus Co, USA
Lima	Baldwin Lima Hamilton Co, USA
Marion	Marion Steam Shovel Co, USA
NBM	Newton, Bean & Mitchell, Bradford
Priestman	Priestman Brothers Ltd, Hull
RB	Ruston Bucyrus Ltd, Lincoln
RH	Ruston & Hornsby Ltd, Lincoln
RP	Ruston Proctor & Co Ltd, Lincoln
R&R	Ransomes & Rapier Ltd, Ipswich
S&P	Stothert & Pitt Ltd, Bath
Taylor Hubbard	Taylor Hubbard & Co Ltd, Leicester
Wh	Whitaker Bros Ltd, Leeds
Wilson	John H. Wilson & Co Ltd, Liverpool

Makers' Number and **Year Built.** These are taken from manufacturers' records in the case of the Ruston companies and from R & R; from operators' records otherwise.

Bucket Capacity and **Jib or Boom Length.** The figures come from operators' records mostly, sometimes from manufacturers. There is no hard and fast rule about the terms 'jib' and 'boom' but generally steam machines are spoken of as having jibs, and diesel and electric machines booms, particularly the larger machines.

Origin. 'New' means that the machine was supplied by the makers to this location. The months quoted are those shown as delivery dates in the makers' records; but very often machines were supplied in sections to be assembled on site (this being particularly so with large machines) so that some time elapsed before they entered service.

Transfers from other locations are shown by bracketed letters and appropriate footnotes. To save space, these footnotes also include details of any changes in bucket capacity or jib length.

Disposal. A machine transferred to another location is shown by a bracketed number and corresponding footnote. Scr = scrapped: s/s = scrapped or sold, disposal unknown. These footnotes also include known details of the individual quarries or working faces that the machine served in the system concerned, with dates where known.

Sources of Information. The principal sources of information consulted and quoted from, using the abbreviations given, are as follows. All were published by Her/His Majesty's Stationery Office.

Mineral Statistics of Great Britain. Robert Hunt.	1853-81	(MS)
Mineral Statistics of Great Britain. Geological Survey Memoirs	1882-94	(MS)
List of Quarries in the United Kingdom and the Isle of Man	1895-1934	(LQ)
Special Reports on the Mineral Resources of Great Britain:		
Part XII—Iron Ore. Geologial Survey Memoirs	1920	(GSM)
The Mesozoic Ironstone of England: The Northampton		
Sand Ironstone	1951	(NSI)
The Mesozoic Ironstone of England: The Liassic Ironstones	1952	(LI)

INDEX

Index

Index